THE HUMAN USE OF THE EARTH

The Human

Use of the Earth

BY PHILIP L. WAGNER

THE FREE PRESS, *New York*

COLLIER-MACMILLAN LIMITED, *London*

FIRST FREE PRESS PAPERBACK EDITION 1964

Collier-Macmillan Canada, Ltd., Toronto, Ontario

Library of Congress Catalog Card Number: 60-7092

printing number
4   5   6   7   8   9   10

J e reconnais l'existence d'une géographie autonome dont nul plus que moi n'apprécie la valeur et l'intérêt: non seulement elle contient une philosophie, comme toute science digne de ce nom, mais elle est presque, en elle-même, une philosophie du monde de l'homme.

—Camille Vallaux,
Les sciences géographiques
(Paris, 1929)

PREFACE

THIS BOOK shows man as the inhabitant and beneficiary of artificial environments, created by human effort and mediating between nature and the human individual. Its purpose is to suggest how different human cultures and social arrangements express themselves in artificial features of landscape, and how these man-made installations affect the life conditions of human individuals and the natural features of the earth.

This theme is both geographical and ecological. It concerns on the one hand the distribution of surface features of the earth and their particular associations, and on the other hand deals with man's relation to environment. These two topics are necessarily complementary. Neither human ecology nor regional geography can progress far without according due attention to the peculiar role of artificial environments in the biology of man and in the whole scheme of nature.

This book is written in the hope of casting some crude bridge over that intellectual chasm that divides the social sciences from the physical and biological disciplines. The geographer, whose tradition has long demanded frequent leaps across this awesome barrier, has every reason to try to improve the facilities for passage. The geographer, too, has to live up to an academic inheritance that includes a strong interest in the larger material works of man, which tend to be overlooked both by social and by natural scientists. (The perennial debate among geographers as to whether or not there is some distinctive object of geographic observation and research might well be resolved, in fact, if the artificial environment were acknowledged as geography's central interest.)

Although no methodological argument is intended, it is to be hoped that both geographers and other readers may find here a notion of the structure and capabilities of the discipline. The ideas put forward in these pages have been developed over some years of observation, reading, and reflection. They are the product of a prolonged and sometimes painful effort to arrive at a satisfactory personal conception of the geographer's discipline, which would combine theoretical consistency, practical significance, and a realistic program for empirical investigation. Clearly this objective has been but incompletely attained, and all that can be offered here is a faulty preliminary sketch map of the territory, of which much is left to be explored.

The argument developed in this book revolves about a few main ideas, as follows:

The human society is a phenomenon of an unusual and peculiar sort within nature. One of its most distinctive features is its creation of and dependence on artificial environments. The creation of artificial environments depends upon particular kinds of relations among men in societies and economies, upon certain ways of regular interaction between men and plants and animals, and upon the vast expansion of the physical powers of the human body through the enlistment of natural forces and natural materials in its service. The living conditions of individuals in a particular society are governed by the interaction of their work with natural processes to create a distinctively modified environment which reflects their culture, social organi-

zation, and techniques, their relations with certain wild or domestic organisms, and the character of the land itself. The
constitution of the artificial environment of a society, and the
location of its components in space as the map shows them,
express all of these influences and in their turn influence the
lives of groups and individuals in a fundamental way. Given a
proper understanding of these several influences, we may one
day aspire to answer some of the questions that our maps ask,
and learn to explain the distribution of artificial features reliably
and concretely, to assess their effects on man, and even to pre-
dict their development and influence.

It would take a full autobiography to give adequate acknowl-
edgment for all the help, inspiration, and ideas that have gone
into the making of this book. It begins in earliest childhood
with my parents' encouragement of curiosity and exploration.
During about twenty years of schooling good teachers have
helped me along the way. A great inspiration and much of my
training are derived from Carl Sauer and his colleagues at
Berkeley, under whom I did my graduate work. Later, at
Chicago, I was confronted with a new and unexpected kind
of geography and was stimulated to an attempt to reconcile
it with the tradition I follow.

While writing and rewriting this book, I have been able to
count on both patient encouragement and discerning criticism
from my wife, Alicja Iwańska. The drafts had the great benefit
of critical reading by several generous friends and colleagues;
it is a pleasure to acknowledge the help of Conrad M. Arensberg, Homer Aschmann, Robert J. Braidwood, Alfred E. Emerson, Andrew Gunder Frank, Eliot Freidson, Daniel R. Fusfeld,
Marshall G. M. Hodgson, Paul B. Sears, Frederick J. Simoons,
Sol Tax, and Eric Wolf, and of my colleagues Wesley C. Calef,
Marvin W. Mikesell and Gilbert F. White. Their thoughtful
criticism and suggestions are much appreciated. Cartographic
work is by Mr. M. J. Huber, and the Department of Geography
of the University of Chicago gave permission to use the base
map. Whatever blunders, blind spots, and obscurities remain
are my own.

CONTENTS

LIST OF FIGURES

THE HUMAN USE OF THE EARTH

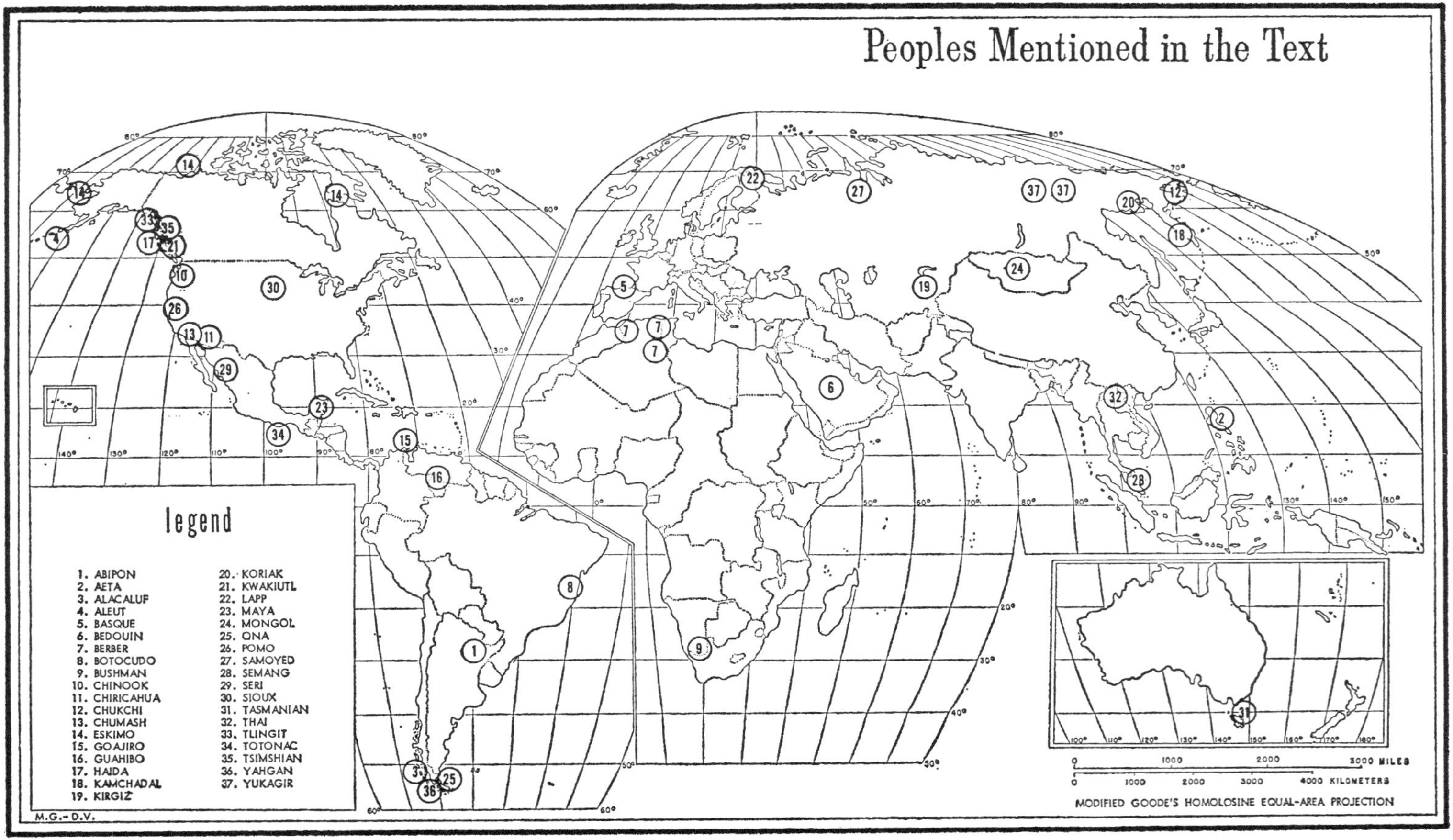
Peoples Mentioned in the Text
legend
1. ABIPON
2. AETA
3. ALACALUF
4. ALEUT
5. BASQUE
6. BEDOUIN
7. BERBER
8. BOTOCUDO
9. BUSHMAN
10. CHINOOK
11. CHIRICAHUA
12. CHUKCHI
13. CHUMASH
14. ESKIMO
15. GOAJIRO
16. GUAHIBO
17. HAIDA
18. KAMCHADAL
19. KIRGIZ
20. KORIAK
21. KWAKIUTL
22. LAPP
23. MAYA
24. MONGOL
25. ONA
26. POMO
27. SAMOYED
28. SEMANG
29. SERI
30. SIOUX
31. TASMANIAN
32. THAI
33. TLINGIT
34. TOTONAC
35. TSIMSHIAN
36. YAHGAN
37. YUKAGIR
0 1000 2000 3000 MILES
0 1000 2000 3000 4000 KILOMETERS
MODIFIED GOODE'S HOMOLOSINE EQUAL-AREA PROJECTION
M.G.-D.V.

Figure 1

INTRODUCTION

AMONG all the branches of human knowledge, that which is called Geography contains the largest single body of factual information. Moreover, the further supply of such information potentially available, but "not yet catalogued," is limitless. No single person can ever hope to know more than a small portion of what it is possible to know about even the mere location of places on the earth's surface.

The professional scholar in geography commonly approaches his subject matter comparatively and synthetically.[1] Geographers do not pride themselves particularly on knowing a great many precise locations. They stress instead the similarities among places and their grouping into larger *regions,* and deal with the distinctive combinations of geographic features that give character to these regions. The concept of the geographic region makes it possible to arrange the vast collection of geographic facts in a convenient way. It permits large descriptive generalizations about the distribution of phenomena over the earth's surface; it also emphasizes the close association and possible connections among the characteristic features of particular localities.

Regional description, however, can tell us only how certain facts are related in space. In cannot show how these facts may be related to each other in additional ways, what their mutual effects may be.[2] Certain of the "systematic" branches of geographic study, like geomorphology, do, indeed, deal with the actual processes that create features of the landscape, and attempt to discover under what conditions such features will tend to be produced. It is already possible for the geomorphologist both to describe and to explain the distribution of many kinds of land-forms, such as hills and mountains, valleys and plains, lakes and streams, though the scientific study of geomorphology is still in its infancy. The geography of several other kinds of physical features, like climates, soils, waters, and plant cover, is being studied with similar success.[3]

Thus, much of the physical diversity of the earth can be interpreted as the result of natural processes that can be identified and measured. The same has not been true of human geography. The works and influences of man come about through technical processes that are mostly well-known, but just when, where, and how these processes may be active remains to be discovered and described.

The human use of the earth, as we all know, does nevertheless proceed in an orderly and reasonable way. All of us are aware of some of the ways in which members of our own society deliberate upon and select certain kinds of locations for roads, bridges, dams, factories, farms, and shopping centers, and we know that many factors may be considered in arriving at these decisions. Even so, there has heretofore been little effort devoted to formulating general propositions about the considerations that govern the location of all of man's creations. Promising beginnings have been made, but they relate to only one kind of human society, for which the pertinent information is uniquely abundant and convenient to use.[4]

The premise upon which this book is built is that there is

an order and regularity in the geography of man's works. We have data in profusion against which this assumption may be tested, but a comprehensive and consistent way of looking at these data has been lacking. The purpose of the book is, therefore, not to present new data or to summarize well-known facts, but rather to lay out an interpretation of man's use of the earth as the orderly function of technical systems which interact with nature under definite limiting conditions.

ENVIRONMENTS AND SYSTEMS

TWO MAJOR conceptual devices familiar to scientists will be employed in examining the processes concerned.[5] These are the ideas of the integrated and on-going *system,* and the *environment* in which it operates. An interpretation constructed upon these two concepts must necessarily fail of exhaustiveness and want in particularity, at least when it concerns a subject so complex and uncontrollable as the social aspects of geography. The sturdy Roman soldier, Ceteris Paribus, who stands guard over so many experimental scientists, cannot defend us against rash error here, and without his watch we can trust only to our own prudence, and can simply forebear to venture too far or covet too much.

The idea of environment is well embedded in the geographic tradition. So much is known of environments that we suffer most of all, perhaps, from ignorance about just what they environ, and where and how their particular effects may count. Much ambitious writing by geographers in the past has all too recklessly leapt from sketchy knowledge of environmental conditions to grandiose assumptions about human life and history. The purging of such "environmentalist" thought from academic geography has been a long and painful process from which we are still only convalescing.[6] Environment, however, is not what earlier geographers imagined—a great enveloping complex "thing" which they had to study, and which "determined" human events. It may better be regarded, I think, as a *way of thinking* about certain things in relation to human events. What is worth maintaining is the idea that some conditions of earth, air, water and wild life are significant for certain things that human beings do, make, have, or are. An environment is only an environment in relation to something that it environs, and is significant insofar as it interacts in some way with that thing. It is no easy matter to discover just where and when, much less how, some property of an environment does have significance for a process in which one may be interested. We do not know much, for instance, about which climatic phenomena affect our health or moods, or how (or even if) the presence of a forest modifies regional climate. But even when the critical environmental variables have been isolated, they may be hard to follow and to measure. Thus, evaporation of moisture from the soil, and transpiration of it from plants, both reduce the water supply of crops, but it is so expensive and cumbersome to measure these things that their rates are not known first-hand for many times or places. Much is known about the gross natural environment of man, but often the very information that would be most significant is unavailable.

A standard method for discovering which environmental properties are significant for a particular process is that of considering the process as a function of a "system." The system is conceived as a set of interrelated variables, such that there are repercussions upon some or all of its member variables each time one of them is subjected to certain kinds of change. When one dials a telephone number, for instance, he sets in motion a series of repercussions in a system of switches and lines which usually produces a connection with the desired party. The stubbing of a toe may cause a mouth far away to say "ouch" or something worse, because the body acts as a system. Geographers are familiar with this idea. They use such terms as "a system of communications," "a system of crop rotation," and "systems of land tenure." The branches of geography that deal with particular kinds of earth features—cities, landforms, climate, vegetation and so forth—are referred to as *systematic* in contrast with *regional* geography, and make more or less explicit use of the concept of systems.

Let us then consider *human geography*—the distribution of

man's works, in particular—as the concrete results of processes going on in systems interacting with environments.

Everyone knows that in different parts of the world there are different sorts of crop fields, houses, shops, and so forth. It must be, therefore, that the processes of their origin represent the operations of many dissimilar technical systems. There are countless evidences that different peoples do things in different ways, and that their many technical systems must be considered individually in order that the diversity of human geography may be understood.

It is clear, too, that differences of natural environment play roles in the operation of technical systems. This is most apparent with relation to farming activities, for as we know, any crop demands a particular combination of soil, climate, and other conditions, and no crop can be grown everywhere on earth. Attention must therefore be focused upon the operation of many different technical systems, working under innumerable natural environments.

Another kind of environment remains to be considered, however. This is the one which most obviously conditions the behavior of the human beings who actually make, operate, and manage all technical equipment: that is, society. Society, in fact, is best regarded not merely as an environment, but as a system in itself, or rather as a whole set of interlocking systems. The societal environment has, like the natural environment, great significance for technical processes under very particular and specific conditions which are not easy to identify. It is helpful to segregate certain sub-systems of society such as "the economy" and "the linguistic community" in order to find the particular conditions that are most intimately connected with the operation of technical processes. This also applies to the natural environment. It is useful to decompose the notion of *climate*, for example, into such elements as *precipitation, atmospheric humidity, temperature, light,* and so on, and to treat each of these as a function of a system.

Pursuing the idea of systems can become a frustrating and fruitless game. That is perhaps why we deal with most things merely as environments of the one particular system in which we are interested at the moment. There is no reason to extend this present study into detailed consideration of all the various possible impinging systems, either of the natural or societal universes. The more modest aim of marking out the major points of contact of natural and societal environments with the various technical systems is quite sufficient. It will be reward enough to discover in the panorama of human geography some evidence of the interplay of societal, technical, and natural influences.

The facts of human geography which must be accounted for consist in man's alterations of and additions to the features of the earth's surface. The features of human origin which are created by technical processes stand out from those of natural origin, that is, from features whose origin and character can potentially be explained by the principles of physical and biological sciences alone. To be sure, it is not always easy to discriminate between natural features in this sense and those produced or affected by man. In many cases it is quite impossible to document the history of doubtful features. It should be plain, too, that nothing happens on earth (except perhaps miracles) that is really contrary to the "laws of nature" in the wider sense; and so, in the last analysis, man's works comprise only a peculiar sector of nature.

Let us distinguish two realms of geographic phenomena, however, despite these reservations. Features of natural origin will be called *natural features,* and those in whose origin man has had a hand will be known as *artificial features.* Considered as they impinge on the life processes of the human body or upon the functioning of human societies, both kinds of features together constitute the *environment.* The common usage of the word "environment" bears this specific meaning.

For purposes of analysis it is helpful to distinguish again between the natural environment and the effects created by man, or the artificial environment. *Artificial environments* are the works of man as they interact with human life.[7] Man "makes himself at home" by arranging and changing his surroundings as best he can to suit his wants. The technical system, under the influence of natural and societal conditions, has already been identified as the instrument of this creative process. It is going to be the business of most of this book to indicate the major kinds of technical systems, and the types of artificial environments this process produces. How, though, can any sense be made of such a wealth of different and distinct ways of using the earth?

Another conceptual device, *typology*, will make it possible to introduce some order into what is known about existing technical systems and artificial environments. Typologies, like environments and systems, are already much used by geographers; they will be employed often in this book. Typology makes unnecessary the comparison of examples or instances point by point in every respect when classifying phenomena. A few critical points of difference in dress and behavior, for example, fortunately enable us to distinguish readily between men and women without subjecting the individuals in question to minute examination. There are certain critical properties of systems and environments that make it possible to distinguish such different types as have practical significance in any particular connection.

It can be discovered empirically that the mobility patterns of a society, for instance, are closely correlated with many other of its features; moreover, this is also clear on simply logical grounds. The way in which people and things move, as members of a system, in relation to the environment both natural and artificial, is the key to the chief typology to be employed.[8]

Patterns of environments and systems will be seen here, in accordance with geographic practice, as arrayed in space, and in time.[9] The overall "frame of reference" in which our questions are stated and our answers sought is the typical geographic one of spatio-temporal co-ordinates on a world or regional scale. The conceptual equipment for the ensuing discussions thus includes the ideas of system, environment, type, and geographic space and time.

The two related subjects of this book can now be elaborated. First: What are the relations between the human body, as a system, and the conditions of its environment, both natural and artificial? And at greater length: What are the relations between different types of artificial environments as systems, and their natural and societal environments?

We shall begin with a consideration of the effects of the environment upon the human organism.

CHAPTER TWO

CONDITIONS
OF HUMAN
LIFE

A HUMAN INDIVIDUAL, like other living things, is very much under the influence of the world around him. Animate and inanimate nature provide the means of man's existence, but they also embody threats against his welfare and survival. The human organism is very sensitive to the natural conditions to which it may be exposed. Likewise, life as a member of a human social group furnishes both supports and safeguards, and entails both pains and perils, for the individual.

Mankind, as subsequent chapters will explain, is unusually capable of governing at least some of the conditions of human existence through technical means. Before discussing the peculiar ability of man to use the earth to his own benefit, though, it is desirable to take stock of the effects that nature, society, and technical improvements are able to exert upon the individual.

MAN'S LIFE WITH NATURE

NATURE has considerable direct effect on man. The human body is expressly fitted out with sensory structures that register specific responses to the surroundings. Nature has a direct effect through man's seeing, hearing, tasting, touching, smelling, and his senses of heat and gravitation. Some of the unique features of the human species, indeed, are founded on the capacity of man to be affected deeply and diversely by the external world and to turn sensory impressions into images, ideas, and memories. However, it is not our business here to discuss the ways in which man construes his sensory impressions and responds to them.

More pertinent to our discussion are the effects on man of the numerous mechanical, climatic, and biotic conditions around him. The body is subject to all the "natural laws" affecting material objects and to special "laws" affecting living matter. Under normal conditions, physical circumstances are taken for granted by man, and only occasionally is he aware of physical difficulty, such as that inherent in crossing a rapid stream or in scrambling over rough terrain. He is usually able to avoid these problems if he wishes.

Man is affected by climatic conditions, though atmospheric and solar radiation conditions over most of the earth are almost always well within his natural tolerances. The ranges of air temperature, humidity, barometric pressure, and of concentration of oxygen and other gases in the atmosphere are safe for humans in most places most or all of the time. Relatively minor variation in these features, however, may produce noticeable effects. The skin becomes chapped and the throat aches in the dry air of the Sahara; the warm and very humid air of the Guinea Coast is unpleasantly oppressive to some people; an American winter indoor atmosphere, poor in oxygen and rich in carbon dioxide, induces yawning, and one containing much carbon monoxide can produce coma and death. Temperatures are below safe tolerance levels for prolonged exposure during some part of the year in countries like Tibet and Peru at higher altitudes or in Greenland or Antarctica in high latitudes, and are above tolerable limits at times under desert conditions. There are numerous such effects known to everyone, but they are unusual except in a few places and for a few periods of the year.[1]

There is evidence that some somatic modification has occurred in peoples subject to the direct effects of adverse climatic conditions for many generations. Some tendency toward constriction of the nasal passages and of the eye opening has been noted among the Eskimo, who are exposed to very low air temperatures. The Indians of the Andes have unusually ample thoracic cavities and a special proportion among the different blood cells as adaptations to high altitude conditions.[2] Some differences among peoples in the density and distribution of sweat glands have been adduced as climatic adaptations. There is no substantial evidence, however, that the present distribution of gross "racial" features like skin color reflects climatic adaptation.[3]

The direct effects of the climatic conditions experienced by most humans are too variable, and their extremes are too rarely beyond human tolerances, for these phenomena to exercise a strong selective effect on human populations. Furthermore, even without artificial protection the human body can function quite satisfactorily in most of the usual climatic situations on earth, and in unusual conditions artificial protection is almost always available. Climate, then, generally has slight effect on man.[4]

However, man suffers catastrophes—those rare circumstances in which climatic or other phenomena of physical nature exercise great direct effects. Fires, lightning, hurricanes and tornadoes, storm waves on the sea, floods, mudflows and avalanches, earthquakes and volcanic eruptions terrify and often destroy man because they are abnormal, unpredictable, and overwhelming. They directly affect him by producing a few appalling disasters every year. While they are neither very common nor very extensive, their toll in lives and goods is high in the localities they strike.[5] Man can moderate or even avert catastrophes by artificial means. By prudent avoidance of certain dangerous spots, building cities to resist earthquakes, channeling floods, and restricting the spread of fires, man has lessened the danger to himself. Catastrophes, in any case, are too infrequent and too localized to be counted among the major direct influences that environments regularly exert.

Biotic phenomena also register direct effects upon the human individual in connection with his bodily processes. The supply of necessary materials for these processes requires the ingestion of water and of certain materials of organic origin. The food supply of man is so intimately linked to his relations with other organisms and with his fellows, and so strongly influenced by technical circumstances that the variety of human diets cannot be understood at all in terms of biological effects alone.[6] It is important to recognize, however, that the frequent consumption of foods of certain categories and in definite amounts is essential to the life of the human individual. The human body requires some proteins, some fats, and some carbohydrates regularly, the amounts depending upon age, condition, and habitual activity. Certain chemical elements like phosphorus and calcium are essential, as well as a number of vitamins. A definite amount of water intake, appropriate to individual conditions, is also vital. Thus, man must necessarily be affected by the environmental supply of these requirements.

Food and water requirements are also affected by man's relations with internal symbiotic flora and fauna. The body is the dwelling place of various kinds of specialized organisms among the viruses, bacteria, fungi, protozoa, sometimes worms of different kinds, and even arthropods. A healthy individual is host to some of these, but is not harmfully affected by them. In disease they interfere dangerously in bodily processes.[7]

The bodily effects of diet, water intake, and the activity of disease organisms are interrelated among themselves and with other influences such as hereditary constitution, exposure to climatic effects, and habitual exertion; but the complex influence of these things on health, efficiency and longevity is beyond our topic here.

LIVING TOGETHER

MAN LIVES as a member of natural communities. Being an animal, man is at least indirectly dependent upon plants for sustenance. He dwells in very intimate association with other animals and plants, and with other men, and is fully involved in the intricate complex of mutual relationships that runs through all of nature.

Symbiotic relations are those in which the life processes of one organism are in some essential way dependent upon other organisms. They may be either *obligate* relations, in which one individual cannot survive independently from other individuals, of the same or another kind; or *facultative* relations, in which an individual may, but need not, take advantage of the presence of some other organism to carry on its life processes.[8] Using a broad conception of symbiosis, we shall speak of it as including 1) *predation,* in which an individual destroys members of its own or another species in seeking its own livelihood; 2) *parasitism,* in which an individual lives at the expense of other organisms without providing direct benefits to them; 3) *mutualism,* in which both individuals involved derive benefit from the relation; and 4) *commensalism,* in which two or more species or individuals of one species depend upon the same habitat conditions, which one or both may help to maintain.

Man is both predator and prey in relation to animal populations. Few humans fall victim now to carnivores, though tigers carry off a few villagers every year in India, and lions and leopards still on occasion stalk human prey in Africa. Swimmers are attacked now and then by sharks, rays, and other predatory fish; and wounded animals occasionally overwhelm an incautious hunter. Man, having long been a hunter, has by now succeeded in exterminating many animal species, and in reducing greatly the numbers of most large mammals. No obligate predatory relation exists between any one predatory animal and man, and though in the past certain human groups were highly dependent upon animals for which they fished or hunted, the dependence was not fixed. Thus, such peoples as the Eskimo who formerly

hunted walrus and seal or caribou have been able to accommodate to other means of livelihood as the animal populations declined under the impact of modern weapons.

Humans are always ultimately dependent upon plants. This
dependence may take any one of several forms. Under the
simplest technical regimes (gathering, collecting and predation), an obligate parasitism, in a loose sense, binds humans to
plant and animal organisms of the habitat. This diffuse kind of
parasitism is not strictly a relation between man and one or a
few definite species, but, given the seasonal variation in availability of natural foodstuffs, may be considered a sort of occasional parasitic relationship with particular species. Localized
plant populations affect the ability of humans to live in an area.
The fate of the Bushman band of gatherers is governed by the
fate of wild plants and animals, for at any one time there are
likely to be few alternatives to the use of a given food source.

The dependence of humans on plants may be effected
through predation upon animals, parasitic gathering of plants,
and through relations of mutualism with plants or animals. The
cultivated plant and the domestic animal are in obligate dependence upon man, whose work is essential in providing them
with the necessary life conditions. Man, in turn, may become
largely or entirely dependent upon his cultivated plants, upon
herds of domestic animals, or upon both. The conditions affecting the welfare of crops and herds then also indirectly affect
man, and man attempts to modify these conditions accordingly.
This obligate mutual relationship is one of the foundations of
most human communities.

The symbiosis of *domestication* has been established with
only a few hundreds of plants, and only a few dozen animals.
Apparently very special characteristics are necessary to make
a species suitable for domestication. To be good domesticates,
plants must offer some useful product, must be capable of pros-
pering under human care and must be able to develop toward
varieties giving better yields under man's selection. Animals, if
their domestication is to succeed, must be capable of losing the
instinctive flight-reaction before man, must tolerate some close
bodily contact, must breed under the watch of man, and must

be able to accept the diet man can provide to them. Not many species of either plants or animals seem to meet these specifications, and very few new domesticates are being added to those acquired in remote antiquity.

Many other plants and animals beside the domestic species are commonly found in the vicinity of men. Most of these are *commensals,* or species requiring some of the same foods or *inquilines* seeking the same kinds of habitats as those which man provides for himself or for his domestic species. One prominent group of these are the desired species which man does not exploit but which he enjoys—the decorative garden plants and animal pets. There is a close connection between the mutual symbiosis of domestication and this particular form of association. Indeed, many of the species concerned in the latter relation have long been domesticated, and one of them, the dog, is probably the earliest of domesticated organisms (though perhaps here the commensal relation is even older.)

Another group of commensals and inquilines is treated with indifference or hostility by man. There are two sorts of these undesired species. One is loosely symbiotic with man in his dwellings, along his paths and roads, on his refuse heaps, and so on; and the other lives with his crops and herds. The former include many of the followers of man we call weeds and vermin; the latter are organisms which, though indifferent with respect to man, are often parasitic with relation to his domestic plants and animals. Many organisms fall into both categories—such as rats, mice, many birds and insects; others are, like cockroaches, exclusively resident in human dwellings; and many organisms are entirely pests of crops or herds, like cattle-ticks, smuts, and weevils. Some plants, of which rye is an example, have developed out of the status of weeds into important crops; others have gone from crops to nuisances. Domestic animals also sometimes turn feral, like the "wild" horses and burros of the Southwest, and the homeless prowling cats of American city alleys.

The mutualistic relation of domestication, the commensal relation with pets and ornamental plants, and even the undesired symbiosis with weeds and pests, are established through long-standing human influence on the habitats of other organisms, either consciously or unconsciously, and through a selection, either deliberate or accidental, of the respective reproductive stock. Human action has been equally effective in guiding the evolution of roadside sunflowers and of lapdogs. The crop plants and farm animals; the crickets and carp and cats we keep as pets; the garden flowers, the kitchen vermin, garden pests, and crop diseases; the birds that wake the city dweller in summer and skunks under suburban porches are all where they are, and sometimes even what they are, partly because of man.[9]

Man's influence is registered to a lesser extent throughout all the natural communities of which he is a part- or full-time member. It is often asserted that there is virtually no virgin forest in the world, man's action having so long and so widely affected forest lands everywhere. Man cuts, burns, culls and clears forest lands almost everywhere they occur, though now more efficiently than in the past. The effect remains, though the action of man has not been so catastrophic for vegetation as for fauna.[10] The direct effect of man and his indirect effect through domestic animals nevertheless have been of major importance in modifying vegetations.[11]

Thus far we have been considering the symbioses of men with other species associated with them in natural communities. Now let us consider in brief the ecological features of relations among men. The existence of a human individual altogether apart from society throughout his entire life is inconceivable. Social relationships are obligate for fully "human" man. We shall see that there is a great variety of possible social bonds, and that not all of them define the same kinds of human groupings. Linguistic, religious, territorial, kin, economic, and other divisions intersect or overlap each other.

It may be useful, if not judicious, to extend the name "commensalism" to those forms of human symbioses in which a large number of individuals depend for livelihood on a single habitat, the creation of which is to some degree the responsibility of all, but in which the regular working units are smaller than, and form parts of, the whole group sharing the habitat. The presence of many different "household" economies in a New Guinea subsistence system, for example, means many different small livelihood symbioses, each on the pattern of full mutuality; yet there is a symbiotic relation binding the whole complex of different small economies into a single society. To distinguish the wider social community in general from associations for livelihood purposes, the term commensalism is reserved.

A second kind of symbiosis among humans is found between hostile groups which either prey upon each other's members or exact regular contributions one from the other. These relationships fit into the meaning of "predation," in the case of Polynesian cannibalism, Philippine headhunting, and the like, or fit the definition of "parasitism" where regular tribute is taken, as with the Mongols of old.

The third and closest form of symbiosis among humans is full "mutualism," which we can equate with constitution of a single economy. There are three possible degrees of symbiosis among men: 1) those in which the mutual relationship which is the economy is much smaller in scope than the society (subsistence); 2) those in which there is a facultative mutual connection between the basic livelihood unit and the larger social group (peasant economies); and 3) those in which the limits of the economic unit and the social unit coincide, and the full obligate mutual relationship prevails throughout (commercial economy). The forms of economic organization will be discussed in detail in Chapter 5.

IMPROVING THE ENVIRONMENT

ONE OF THE chief properties of the symbioses formed between men and other organisms, and among men, is their capacity to affect the use of environment. Man's creation of mutualistic relationships in particular—those effected through domestication of plants and animals, and that brought about through establishment of a commercial economy—transforms his livelihood patterns and ultimately brings far-reaching consequences in human living conditions. The relation of an individual to his environment, under these symbioses, is mediated by two sets of influences, the social and the technical, but it is, in the last analysis, still a question of the mechanical, climatic and biotic effects of the total environment on the individual. The technical efforts of man are directed toward improving the natural circumstances for life. Human work serves to alter mechanical, climatic, and biotic features of the immediate environment in order to provide a more favorable artificial situation.

A part of human work is devoted to the production of objects which serve as artificial micro-environments for individuals and small groups. These *facilities* are designed to afford more safe or comfortable local climatic conditions, like dwellings, or to shield the body against climatic rigors, like clothing. The same facilities also guard their users against predatory beasts, dirt, and to a varying degree against minor catastrophes of nature. They often carry symbolic value as well, and clothing, for example, expresses aesthetic taste, pride, ambition, and subtle come-hitherness. The climatic modification effected by the use of closed living spaces is considerable, especially where there are auxiliary facilities for heating and cooling the air. The people of the eastern United States endure on the whole higher temperatures in winter (indoors) than in summer, and even the Eskimos keep their igloos hot. The microclimatology of buildings is a vast and little-known subject, but we may surmise that the interior climate of most kinds of buildings used by different human groups is about as follows: temperature mostly equal to or above prevailing outside temperature (except where thick walls are used, as in the Mediterranean area and Near East); humidity usually above the level of the open air; oxygen concentration considerably lower than outside, and carbon dioxide and other minor gases far more abundant; noxious odors very prevalent.[12] Dwellings to a varying degree serve to exclude objectionable animal predators and pests, to protect the inhabitants against hostile humans, and to hold out winds and dust. On the other hand, they often harbor their own commensal vermin, and in them wastes accumulate to such an extent that in some cases the huts are so choked with filth and detritus that periodic moves to a new site are required.

Clothing shares some of these features.[13] Though it provides protection against rain, cold, sun, insects, and exterior dirt, it sometimes harbors a vicious fauna of its own, and accumulates the exudates of the wearer's body.

Man creates a second kind of artificial effect through the mechanisms that supply goods to individuals. Most productive facilities, in the broadest sense, are devoted to this purpose. The most rudimentary of these facilities are the *containers* present in abundance in most societies, in which food, water and other things are stored. Baskets, nets, pots, barrels, tanks, chests, closets, warehouses and so on make materials available for use over some considerable time. Sufficient and suitable containers must be at hand, indeed, for a substantial and enduring dwelling to be inhabitable. Containers therefore play an important role in improving living conditions.

As we shall see, one of the strategies by which supplies of goods and services become available for actual use is the movement of the would-be consumers themselves to the sources of goods or services. There are even objects that act as containers of man himself, which move over land, across water or through the air, delivering the individual to the places at which he can obtain goods he desires, or where he will be served as he wishes.

The technical means of movement make available to the individual a much wider range of goods and services. Ecologically speaking, even very primitive man is an extremely far-ranging creature. Men have migrated far more widely than almost any other animals. The artificial transport facilities are at least partly responsible for this fact. They have enabled man to travel long distances and cross difficult areas, and have enabled him to take along containers full of reserve goods, which permitted survival in strange or barren environments.

The supply of goods is influenced by man's use of facilities for moving materials. This is especially true of the complexes of artifacts used in production: transport lines, storage facilities, tools, machines, and so on.

The ability of man to deliver goods at the right place and at the right time is only part of his ecological advantage; he also derives great power from his ability to change the form and composition of things to suit his needs. The processing and assembly operations so used in manufacture greatly increase the usefulness of materials to man. He literally creates new goods out of substances unusable as they occur in nature. Manufacture adds vastly to the wealth upon which men can draw by making more things usable. It confers the status of resources upon things that are of no benefit to any other animal.

Manufacture has not yet provided many substitutes for the food materials furnished by plants and animals, either wild or domestic. Man's work, however, has made better ecological circumstances not only for himself but for his domesticates. He has made dwellings for domestic animals, as for himself. A system of transport serves their needs as his. The cultivated field becomes a sort of container holding reserves of all the materials needed by a growing plant, and also a protected site for its growth where pests and competitors are held at bay. Materials are manufactured, transported, stored, and made available to the plants and animals.

The supply of services is as important as the supply of goods. Medicine, hygiene and public sanitation in particular exert a beneficial effect, protecting individuals from mechanical, climatic, and biotic hazards, or correcting the harm sustained from them. Other services like military defense and police protection are considered vital protective features in more complex societies; education, communication, and many more have important secondary ecological effects.

In summary, the ecological conditions of human life are in considerable degree artificial in any society in proportion to the prevailing technical level and degree of economic integration of the society. The conditions of man's bodily existence are modified most widely by his clothing; next by dwellings, containers that accompany them, and by vehicles and craft. The level is also affected by his symbiotic mutual relation with domestic plants and animals, by widespread transport and manufacture, and finally by full economic integration. These factors act cumulatively. They are abetted by growth of the complexity of productive artifacts, by the acquisition of new forms of energy to work under human guidance, and by the realization of new resources.

The degree of technological development, and therefore, the level of artificiality of the environment of man, is at its highest in communities where immense urban settlements have taken root, feeding on a continual supply of goods moving in a multitude of ways from an ever-expanding galaxy of resource sites. The relative concentration of human beings in settlements is in fact a good index to artificiality. Another good indicator is the volume of natural resources used and the variety thereof. Yet another is the relative dependence of individuals upon highly specialized productive roles and the fragmentation of their social relations into many small, discrete, and unconnected parcels.

Those same features of the most complex human communities which indicate their ecological advantages also suggest an unusual degree of inherent ecological risk. Such communities are complex and delicately balanced, and depend utterly upon their artificiality. They and the individuals in them are threatened by the same biological penalties that attend any highly specialized system or species. Their very technical perfection may destroy them in time as other high specializations have destroyed many former species of animals and plants.

Concentrated settlements are vulnerable to both internal disruption and external destruction. Even a strike, particularly a transport strike, can punish and imperil a modern big city. Civil war can become a disaster. Modern large-scale war has made it easy to atomize a great city. And if the right city were chosen, how neatly a whole economy could be shattered, a great industrial system paralyzed!

Another potential threat to concentrated settlements which could also become active in connection with civil disturbance or war is the rapid spread of disease among large populations. Microbes evolve quickly, and medicine races with them. Both the specific precautions against a given strain of bacteria or virus, and the general controls on sanitation (waste disposal, housing conditions, water supply, food handling, etc.) must constantly be maintained at a high level in a densely settled modern city. Thus, man must further refine his environment, for if some unexpected and virulent pathogenic organism runs loose, disaster may occur.

A further threat stemming from high levels of artificiality,

the real import of which is not yet by any means fully comprehended, is the exhaustion or destruction of critical resources
for production or direct consumption. Not only are metals,
fuels, and cultivable soils of concern, water and air pollution are
already very great threats in some industrial areas, having led
to some fatalities and costing ever more to correct. The judicious management of natural resource use is a difficult task which
will forever be a serious problem to countries using resources
in huge volumes.[14]

The psychological and moral impact of modern social conditions upon individuals is another source of man-made vulner-
ability. Demoralization and social disintegration may constitute
another possible source of weakness in complex societies.

ENVIRONMENTS

WE HAVE, thus far, considered the ecological position of man
under conditions of the natural environment, that is under such
conditions as impinge upon him directly without artificial modification, as well as in artificial environments brought about deliberately by man.

The problem in ecology of defining the relations between
men and environments, and of describing precisely the processes
that are the content of these relations, becomes immensely complicated because of the peculiarities of man as an organism.

Nevertheless, it is worthwhile to attempt to introduce some
order into our thinking about environments. The subject of
physical environment is too vast a subject; merely to sketch it
would be insolent and would tell us little about the ecological
position of man, since artificial features are interposed between
individuals and physical nature. Having given some brief consideration to man's peculiar ecology, we shall turn to the task
of accounting for its artificial circumstances.

The first problem, then, is that of noting man's peculiarities
as an organism, and of studying the roles these qualities play
in his creation of a special human relationship with environments. Man's distinctive place in nature is, therefore, the subject
of the next chapter.

MAN'S PLACE
IN THE WORLD

As CARL SAUER WRITES, "there can be no human geography that does not concern itself with communities as associations of skills."[1] Man is a social and a technical animal; his place in nature is peculiar because of the artificial environments he is able to create. Man-made features of environment almost universally mediate the relation between individual humans and the rest of nature. The artificial elements of man's environment are obvious and have often been described, but their relation to the social and technical principles of which they are expressions and which guide their operation have been but little considered.

Groups of men, organized in different ways and using different means, modify and utilize the properties of environments. They affect their habitats and are in turn affected, through the habitats that they themselves create, by nature. The purposive interactions of men with their environments in *work* are especially important. As Harlan Barrows put it, "the relationships between man and the earth which result from his efforts to get a living are in general the most direct and intimate."[2] These relations contribute to the "regional differentiation of the earth's surface" through the localization of particular kinds of human work and works— "the union of a fragment of earth with a group of humanity."[3]

PHYSICAL MAN IN PHYSICAL NATURE

BEFORE WE can deal with man's work and its consequences, the place of man in physical nature in general, and among living beings in particular, needs to be considered. The mechanical properties of the human body and the social characteristics of human aggregations form the common human physical and biological foundation of all the cultural diversity that expresses itself so richly in human geography.

The behavior of man that affects the physical world must be physical behavior, no matter what other influences play upon it.[4] Learned habits (culture) influence behavior, but it is only its physical characteristics that can explain its physical effects. Furthermore, the behavior that affects the physical world is that of individuals; and though the effects of individuals' behavior are contingent on other's acts, complementary to them, and cumulative with them as organized within societies, the individual is the unit of action. Only those influences that affect the individual can explain his behavior or, taking all individuals together, the effects of a whole society's behavior.[5]

The direct influence of man on nature is exerted either through the mechanical effects of his bodily movements, or through devices that magnify and modify them. The human body is a tremendously versatile mechanism, capable of a great many different mechanical operations, many of which can be carried on simultaneously with a high degree of coordination. The power employed by this mechanism is internally supplied, and can be applied over a wide range of intensities. Precision in movement and in the application of energy can be highly developed, and control is enhanced by the continuous flow of information from the sensory apparatus. The mechanical functioning of the body responds to the guidance of conceptual thought, and its sequences and patterns therefore may achieve a great complexity without loss of co-ordination. Moreover, the human body can be changed through the use of tools from a versatile and highly generalized mechanism into a very restricted and efficient specialized one without permanent organic change.

Nature influences action because human action is participation in natural processes. The result of action is affected by man's behavior in conjunction with all the other elements with which it interacts. The same behavior performed in different natural contexts leads to different kinds of results. What humans do is certainly not simply determined by outside nature; but action takes place as physical events within nature, and forms parts of connected and interdependent processes of the physical world. The result of any physical event is not uniquely determined by any one of the several forces entering into it, but is a product of their joint interaction. When we speak, therefore, of the "results" of human action, we mean the results of natural processes in which human action intervenes.

Human physical action cannot completely dominate physical processes and assure the chosen results in every case. Some natural processes are completely beyond human control. But the human role in nature is as close to determining results as human shrewdness and strategy can make it.

Man is also influenced directly by the natural wants of his own body. The things that men require for life—their "needs," or better, their wants—are not simply biological necessities, however. Human wants vary in definition from one group to another and even from one individual to another. They change during the lifetime of an individual and in the course of the history of a society. There is, in fact, a great diversity of conceptions of "normal human wants" among the peoples of the world. But though wants or needs do not merely express direct biological necessities, there is obviously a biological control on human life. Biological requirements set minimum limits on livelihood needs. Any organism which does not make sufficient and appropriate provision for survival must perish. At almost all places and times, human standards of consumption have lain well within the biological limits for survival; any standard otherwise conceived would soon disappear, along with those who held it.

Human wants are generally considered to include those for such things as food, clothing, and shelter. However, they also appear to include many other things that are matters of preference. Under their normal life conditions, in fact, human beings may be said to "want" the services of a particular kind of artificial environment and the goods it provides, and to be more sensitive to social than to physiological pressures in recognizing wants.

SOCIETIES IN NATURE

SOCIAL HABITS and their concomitant artificial environments are highly characteristic of human beings. These attributes, and their combination with other peculiar human features, give man a very distinctive position among living beings. The biological position of man in nature, and its implications for man's geographic role, however, are best understood in the light of what is known of other living beings. A review of some characteristics of plant and animal life is therefore in order at this point.

The stationary plant is dependent on conditions at its site of growth for survival. The raw materials available to the plant for growth are those present at its immediate site or carried to it by atmospheric movements, gaseous diffusion, moving waters, or mobile organisms. It is at the mercy of one physical and chemical environment. The plant itself has relatively little influence over temperature, humidity, light, or other conditions of its surroundings as they affect it, though it may influence greatly the environmental conditions of nearby organisms, and be strongly influenced by them. It must succeed in place or die.

The mobile animals, on the other hand, select environments for particular life processes. They expend large amounts of energy, and their movement imposes mechanical limitations on the forms that their bodily growth may take. Animals are distinguished from most plants by their inability to synthesize food directly from inorganic matter, and, ultimately, are dependent on plants for food. Their mobility appears to be a necessary consequence of this.

Considering geographically the behavior of the mobile animals, with the mammals, man's closest kin, especially in mind, we arrive at a notion that their occupance of habitat is guided by the sensory recognition of places. Mobile animals discriminate among places in the habitat, selecting the feeding grounds and resting places of their kind. They move among particular sites of food supply and other situations in the habitat where physical conditions are favorable for their life processes. One of the leading students of animal behavior tells us that most animals "are confined within a regular network of localities, where for generations they have wallowed, bathed, fought, grazed, mated, slept, etc." They live "in a fixed space-time system, i.e., in a pattern of fixed points, at which they perform definite functions at definite times."[6]

The animal gathers its vegetable food or preys upon other animal species during its movements among the particular places at which they occur throughout the habitat. Many animals seek out special conditions for their lairs, nests, burrows, hives, and other protected resting and mating places. Each kind of animal in a given habitat has a characteristic range and pattern of movements appropriate to its body size, the nature of its diet, and its resting, reproductive, and other habit patterns. The range and patterns of its movements depend mainly on the supply of food materials and the local population of its species, and are often restricted within an established territory which the animal defends and in which it is practically confined.[7]

Regular movements among particular sites and along particular routes in the habitat are thus essential to the survival and efficiency of the animal. It is not a passive role the animal takes; by his very movements he actively modifies his habitat. His environment therefore becomes somewhat artificial. Not only trails and dwelling places, but also hoards of foodstuffs testify to animals' creation of artificial conditions for their own use. Members of some species such as field mice and wood-peckers employ storage in caches to provide concentrated supplies of food to last beyond the natural harvest time. Some organisms even gather and protect a population of other plant and animal species which supplies food as needed. The most spectacular instance of this behavior apart from man, perhaps, is that of the ants that keep fungus gardens. Bees and termites are examples of animals that transform materials chemically or modify them physically for use. These manufacturing processes are usually specifically linked with the physiology of the animal body and are controlled by inherited aptitudes and behavior patterns.[8]

Living things dwell in mutual dependence and form a mantle of life over the inorganic fundament. The organisms of each locality are closely adjusted to the external conditions of their habitat. The agglomerations of plants and animals in each place are themselves somewhat structured and constant in composition and form, and tend to induce some modification in the exterior environments of their individual members.[9] *Communities* of living things are characterized by elaborate relations of interdependence among their members. In them, the organic materials created by plants are transferred from one individual to another—from plant to plant through parasitism and saprophytism, and especially from plants to animals, while the latter are preyed upon and consumed by other animals in turn. Life does not surrender easily the materials that it seizes upon and builds with, but passes them on from one living being to another within the community; even the metabolic wastes of one organism become the food of others, and finally death releases the organic substances of the plant or animal body to nourish other organisms.

In addition to food supplies, such conditions as light, temperature, moisture, shelter, and mechanical support are specifically necessary for each plant or animal species in the community. For each kind of living being there is usually only one "niche" or individual kind of habitat having its own peculiar life conditions and its own distinctive role in the life of the community.

The conditions under which one individual lives are the product of influences and interactions among many other organic and inorganic forces in its environment. Each organism contributes its part according to its form and functioning. The different roles of organisms are the consequences of genetic differences. The community is thus created and maintained by the integration of many specialized individual functions, and the division of functions among its members is along genetic lines.

Some kinds of communities include large aggregations of members of single animal species.[10] Each of the individuals may perform the same function within the community, or the roles of individuals may be specialized within the species. There is some degree of specialization of role in any species that reproduces sexually, of course, and this specialization often goes beyond the act of reproduction to include differences in the part taken in constructing the dwelling and caring for the young. A restricted specialization of this kind is likely to be characteristic within a group of family size, composed of mating pair and young offspring. Often this kind of role specialization has little special effect on environment.

The individual organism must, on the one hand, be specialized enough in function to exploit some particular conditions in the habitat, so as to occupy a niche that no other organism can contest with it; and it must, on the other hand, possess enough versatility to adapt to any conditions of environment that may impinge upon its life activities. These two requirements may be thought of as polar extremes of a continuous scale, and every species may be placed somewhere along the scale between specialization and versatility. Some of the disadvantages of commitment to either specialization or versatility are overcome by *aggregation* of organisms into larger groups within the community.

One simple form of aggregation is the *herd* or *flock*, in which individual roles are very slightly specialized, chiefly for reproduction and defense, and the effects of all individuals on the environment are more or less alike. The advantage of membership is the protection afforded by preponderance of numbers.

Herd animals are usually mobile over large expanses of territory, and are often migratory. The herd may be entirely of one species, or of several.

Other aggregations are made up of specialized individuals of a single species performing several different roles. In this kind of aggregation the division of labor contributes primarily to the welfare of the group as a whole rather than to the maintenance of individuals. The specialized activity of individuals exploits efficiently the various properties of the environment, and the effect is to produce a collective artificial environment for all the various individuals in the species. This environment is itself versatile in meeting various environmental conditions.

There are two types of stable aggregations which are composed of differentiated individuals of the same species. One is the *colony,* made up of specialized individuals of various kinds within the species, all of which have lost the power of locomotion. Although it achieves both versatility and specialization, a colonial aggregation such as corals shares the disadvantages of plants in being stationary. Animal colonies are therefore successful only in the seas or in other liquid media where the movements of the medium itself make individual mobility less necessary.

Societies are the second type of animal aggregation in which the roles of individuals of the same species are greatly differentiated. Among social animals, highly specialized behavior of each individual contributes distinctively to the establishment and upkeep of an artificial environment. Individual social behavior is integrated with the activity of other individuals serving the same function in other ways.

The artificial environments created by social animals are greatly more complex and stable than those of non-social mobile animals. Because considerable specialization of activity is possible for individuals in a social species, they can accomplish more different kinds of modification for the benefit of all. The effect of these modifications, integrated by social organization, is cumulative rather than alike and limited for each individual. Individual non-social animals produce parallel and repetitive effects in their respective environments; but social animals produce joint and cumulative effects.

The roles of individuals in a social species of animals are characterized by close association with particular site and route patterns. Places and roles are co-ordinated.

The relation of individuals of a social species to the artificial environment of their community has two aspects. First is the contribution of individual behavior to the construction and maintenance of the artificial environment. Second is the contribution of the environment to the sustenance and protection of the individual. Most of the behavior of the individual in the most "specialized" species has little to do with its own immediate survival; most of the means of its survival are not the product of its own immediate behavior. The behavior of social animals, in other words, must be seen both as *production,* leading to the establishment and operation of the artificial environment, and *consumption,* the use of that environment to sustain individual life. This principle applies as much to man as to other social beings.

There are highly social species among ants, bees, termites, wasps, and man. In all of the insect societies, the specialization of individual functions is made possible by physiologic or anatomical differences determined genetically or induced by physical conditions affecting bodily development. The artificial environment created by any insect society is always of a type characteristic of the species; the only variation in form, apart from those due to external circumstances, is that introduced by genetic change and developed under the pressure of selection. Individuals are incapable, by and large, of spontaneously changing their roles very far to adapt to changing circumstances.

The societies of men are unlike insect societies in one feature of great consequence: specialization is not determined genetically or physiologically within them. Individuals can change their roles, and the species or portions of it can change the kinds of artificial environments they create and inhabit. There are more different sorts of individual roles in a human than in an insect society, and there are a great many more varieties of

artificial environments in use by the single human species than
in all societies of insects put together. The artificial environments
of human societies are most frequently composed of much more
diverse individual subunits, and in all respects, reflect much
more complexity than do those of insects.

CULTURE IN NATURE

HUMAN SOCIETIES also differ profoundly from insect societies
in their constitution and their effects. Man, as a mammal, attains
a much greater bodily size and strength than any insect and
thus can produce proportionately greater effects in nature by
individual action. The mammalian body, furthermore, has a
vastly more highly developed muscular system than the insect's,
and is therefore much more versatile. Mammalian and especially
human nervous systems are incomparably more complex and
efficient. Man's life span is much longer and is not divided into
a series of radically different stages like those of most insects.
These and other somatic differences make it possible for humans
to intervene much more massively in nature and to regulate their
actions in quite different ways from those possible for insects.
The mechanisms of communication in particular are decisive.

The peculiarities of the human nervous system allow a high
development of symbolic communication. The transmission of
stimuli from one organism to another is nothing unusual, nor is
the recognition of symbols peculiar to man alone.[11] What is
distinctive is the constant use of symbolic stimuli that are both
precise and flexible and capable of achieving a very complex
integration of behavior among great numbers of individuals.
Humans learn to recognize and respond to the symbolic content of a particular set of stimuli in a consistent way that may
be called *culture*.

A *culture* is any one such set of stimuli which serves as
a vocabulary of perception. It consists of a large but finite set
of agreed categories which identify, interpret, and relate the
phenomena of experience, generalizing from the unique event
to the classifying concept. Any of the categories or meanings

applied under a given culture to experience embraces a range
of situations conceived as possible, and sets limits within which
appropriate discriminations among phenomena are made. Cultural categories release perception from the bonds of space and
time; they make possible the arrangement of experience in an
abstract order other than that imposed by the spatio-temporal
continuum. A culture is thus an instrument of abstraction and
imagination.[12]

Through abstraction the properties of experienced things
may be considered, and relations among them may be inferred,
altogether outside the physical and concrete universe of action.
The abstracting function enables men to project and recall experience (or rather symbols of perceived experience) and so to
plan and hope and learn. Though the orientation of behavior
in terms of past and future events is not altogether lacking among
animals, and is in a way presupposed by their spatial mobility,
the ability to think back and to think ahead is much more highly
developed in man. Only man has truly possessed and mastered
time.

Cultures are cumulative. They translate human experience
into an expanding store of symbols that preserve meaning and
relation in abstract and readily transmitted forms. Language,
in the wider sense, is a storehouse of cultural categories that
preserve and fix the meanings of the past experience of individual humans through conventional symbols. Human language
and other symbols can communicate the existence and even the
specific properties of things that cannot be apprehended immediately by the senses, or even of "things" that do not exist.
(The word for "no" is perhaps the most human word in any
language.)

Symbolic behavior provides a means of equating the under-
standings and organizing the behaviors of many human individuals as social groups. A major part of human activity is
channeled and guided by cultural symbols. It is integrated into
behavior patterns of larger agglomerations of individuals who
share common cultures and whose relationships are structured
as societies.

HUMAN GEOGRAPHY

THE PECULIAR position of human societies in the world is now, perhaps, more intelligible. We began by postulating that:

1.) Man is a natural phenomenon, that is, that his body is a physical object and that some of his actions are physical and biophysical events. The actions of man have concrete results in the material world; and, in turn, the material conditions under which action takes place influence its results.

We have also seen that:

2.) Man is a social animal of a special kind. He forms culturally organized societies wherein similar individuals perform different specialized functions, and dwell in environments that the group artificially establishes and maintains. We speak of "societies" not "colonies" because the individuals composing them are mobile rather than sessile. The specialization of these individuals is a differentiation in typical behavior, but they are genetically, structurally, and physiologically nearly undifferentiated. They form aggregations: that is, they occur contiguously in space and simultaneously in time, jointly affect a common habitat, and are reciprocally affected by it. Such aggregations are so organized that the specializations of individual behavior are mutually contingent, and complementary and cumulative in their effects; humans work together. They are organized culturally through the use of equivalent communicable symbols by all their members.

Human geography is largely concerned with the consequences of the third circumstance, which is that:

3.) Cultures differ. As they differ, so the symbolic contexts in which men live and think and act will differ, and so the behavior of men will take particular forms for each cultural group. A cultural tradition, with its own ways of thinking and seeing, and with its own conceptions of human nature, and aspirations and the means of their fulfillment, is shared by a group of human beings. Such a group of persons, from a few individuals to many millions, commonly not only shares a culture, but also forms an interacting social unit.

Community of culture, occupation of a single kind of habitat, and participation in the same society lead to similarities in behavior among individuals. The patterning of sites of activity and routes of movement then tends to be characteristic and nearly uniform (that is, to fall within certain limited ranges) for all individuals in certain categories or statuses within a given society, and, taken all together, for the society as a whole.

These patterns are not pure abstractions, for they tend to impress themselves visibly and concretely in nature. The net of sites and routes that marks a habitat of some distinct group of humans is produced by a manner of utilization and modification of environment that is distinctive of that group.

The bases of the constitution and function of the human social groups themselves must be sought in certain idiocratic features of the human species. These are, in part, plainly related to some general mammalian characteristics. The next chapter deals with these foundations of societies in man as expressed geographically.

HUMAN SOCIETIES AS GEOGRAPHIC FORMS

A HUMAN society consists of a population which occupies a more or less continuous territory, and whose members communicate among themselves in the terms of a symbolic tradition or culture, and form organized groups for common action.

Mankind is divided into a great many more or less distinct and self-contained societies, but all human beings form a single potential interbreeding population; all are potentially capable of communicating with any of their fellows; and a single pervasive "web" of organized relations reaches out to link most men at least loosely together.[1] Probably few human individuals have lived since infancy altogether outside of social relations and managed to survive for long,[2] and few are the societies that are without any contact with their neighbors. The societies of men in existence today are therefore only relatively autonomous and sovereign. They are enough so, however, so that vast dissimilarities exist among them, and their various ways of living and of work find a multitude of distinctive regional expressions.

(38)

THE BOND OF LANGUAGE

INTERACTION AND JOINT ACTION among the members of a society require a regulatory mechanism, which takes the form of *symbolic communication*. Resting upon community of culture, the symbolic communication of human beings includes a large part of their total behavior, of which language is but one part devoted exclusively to the functions of expression and communication. Individual societies tend to be coextensive with distinctive linguistic communities, and the distribution of each language is likely to coincide with that of a corresponding society.[3] The correlation between language and society is far from perfect, however. It is possible for one individual to know and use more than one language, for instance, without belonging to two societies. A single language may be the medium of communication of several societies, as are English, French and Spanish. Also, one society may consist largely of monolingual speakers of several different tongues like those of Switzerland, Belgium, Canada or the Soviet Union.

The degree of linguistic homogeneity in a human group tends to reflect the intensity of past or present social intercourse and interaction. Normally a group of persons who are in frequent daily contact speak more or less alike. Usually the language of the household or "mother tongue" is counted as the basic one of a person, and the group of people with whom one habitually communicates in this language is one's primary linguistic community. The members of a speech community possess at least two things in common: they know how to recognize and reproduce a certain set of speech sounds, the phonemes of their language; and they are aware of similar symbolic meanings attached to these sounds and to particular combinations of them. They also share a common vocabulary of extra-linguistic symbols—like facial expressions, bodily postures, gestures, and the like—and recognize and use common symbolic values in objects and events. The face-to-face group of habitual intercourse, interaction, and communication is, therefore, the smallest sociolinguistic unit.

Local speech forms tend to be distinctive but often resemble closely those of neighboring groups. Speech practices vary gradually with spatial and social distance from group to group. The speech forms of many local groups, varying somewhat among themselves, may be grouped together as dialects, and dialects in turn into languages. Each dialect or language usually corresponds to a given territory and to a given population. Eventually, because of historical circumstances, sharp spatial discontinuities between speech groups are met with which represent the boundaries of major communities of linguistic descent. Thus, within the area of Austria and Germany there is a gradual transition between local dialects, from Styria to the North Sea. A peasant from Tyrol might find it hard to understand an old-fashioned fisherman from the Baltic, though they speak dialects of the same stock, but each can understand the dialects neighboring on his own. Southeast of Styria, though, lies altogether alien speech, Slovenian, which cannot be understood at all by neighboring monolingual speakers of German dialects. On the borders of the great German dialect area are languages only remotely related to German, if at all—French, Italian, Romansh, Friulian, Slovenian, Croatian, Hungarian, Czech, Polish; Danish and Frisian are closer; and Dutch and Flemish are part of the world of German dialects.

Other forms of language than the habitual local idioms are the vehicles of communication among larger social groups and over more extensive territories. Today these often overshadow or replace the distinctive local dialects. These languages of wider employment may be called "standard" languages, and their distribution coincides with that of the larger social units to which they correspond. Among them are "national" languages that belong to large, politically integrated populations and sometimes prevail over large areas—such as French in France and English in most of Great Britain, which have succeeded most of the dialects and left only a few unassimilated areas of alien speech (Provençal, Basque, Breton, Alemanic German, and Flemish in France, and Welsh and Scots Gaelic in Britain). There are also "literary" languages and their spoken "colloquial" forms belonging to communities defined by a common literary tradition, such as Arabic over most of North Africa and the Middle East, or Mandarin over China. "Special" languages like slang, cant, argot, and liturgical tongues are identified with particular groups or particular functions in a society, exemplified by GI military slang, and "journalese," on the one hand, and traditional ritual languages like Hebrew, Sanskrit, Latin, Old Church Slavic and Syriac on the other. Man also uses languages of intergroup communication special to commerce and contact situations, like Pidgin in Melanesia, Sabir in the Mediterranean, the former Chinook jargon along the Columbia River, and such tongues as Latin, Greek, Arabic and Aramaic, each of which has served as a lingua franca in the past.

All languages and forms of language perform a necessary social function: a speaker implies a listener. The bond effected by the use of language therefore presupposes some degree of equivalence in the symbolic content of speech and other symbolic behavior among those who communicate. Equivalence is always a relative thing; nobody can transmit fully to another all the associations that a particular word or idea has for him. Within a face-to-face group—including the vast masses reached and "homogenized" by modern communications engineering—equivalence can be fairly high. Between members of speech groups of related descent equivalence is sufficient for most needs of everyday communication. Between speakers of different languages, however, equivalence is insufficient for most communication, and recourse must then be had to translation or to one common auxiliary tongue.

LINGUISTIC GEOGRAPHY AND
GENETIC CLASSIFICATION

SEVERAL FEATURES of the geographic distribution of languages are pertinent to the problems of human geography.[4] One is the conventional "genetic" classification of languages by which languages and even dialects are grouped according to inferred descent. On a local scale, this kind of classification shows the prevalence of minor differences even between adjacent villages in long-settled countries. On a world scale, the genetic map of languages shows the widespread distribution of a few major linguistic stocks like Indo-European, Turkic, Sino-Tibetan, Semitic, Niger-Congo,[5] Siouan, Uto-Aztecan, Malayo-Polynesian, Athapascan, and Arawakan. Each such stock, of course, usually includes many mutually unintelligible individual languages. Many much more restricted distributions occur alongside these. The *linguistic museums,* as someone has called them, of areas like the Caucasus, the eastern Sudan and Ethiopia, New Guinea, Southeast Asia, primitive California, Oaxaca, and the eastern slopes of the Peruvian and Ecuadorian Andes are full of such small and isolated linguistic units. Another type of patchwork distribution of languages is represented in cases like that of Macedonia, where the local Slavic dialects are spoken in some villages, while Greek, Albanian, Turkish, and Vlach (Romanian) are used in others. Romany is spoken by the wandering Gypsies and a dialect of Spanish by the Jews in the larger towns and cities.

The relationships attested in the patterns of language distribution are of great historical interest, but cannot be taken to imply close cultural similarities or racial kinship among all groups now speaking related tongues. In the Americas, both the civilized Aztecs and the Shoshonean hunters of the Western deserts spoke languages of the same stock; and the speech differences between the Yakut reindeer herder and the Turkish businessman of Istambul, or between Hollanders, Sicilians, and Kurds fall within the scope of single linguistic stocks. We know that individuals and peoples change their languages. The influx of all sorts of people into the United States, for example, has made almost all into English-speakers, regardless of previous language.

There is reason to believe, however, that in the past the link between language and ancestral culture was stronger, and that change took place less frequently and less absolutely because of isolation. Even without outside interference languages do change with time, however, and many peoples have switched languages in the past. Most rapid and deep change has no doubt occurred in civilized areas, as in the Middle East, where Sumerian, Akkadian, Aramaic, Persian, Turkish, Greek, and Arabic have held wide sway for long periods. In more isolated and uncivilized parts of the world there have been fewer and less radical changes, and so there is indeed in some places a parallel between linguistic and other cultural features. The most decisive and frequent kinds of linguistic replacement are those in which peoples formerly speaking isolated languages of very local distribution have gone over to great languages of wide currency; these transferences are likely to be accompanied by extensive cultural change. There are cases of very rapid, repeated changes of language in the face of advancing cultural contact. Examples of this were the shift in Anatolia from local languages to Greek and then to Turkish, and the replacement among some tribes of the Sayan Mountains of a Samoyedic speech by Turkic in the nineteenth century, and of the Turkic speech by Russian a few decades later.[6]

Linguistic kinship is important to keep in mind, for it plays a part in history and influences geography directly when it becomes the basis of self-conscious movements like Pan-Germanism, Pan-Turkism, and the Jugoslav unity movement. In some places a new "national" language is created as a basis for a single nationhood of linguistically related peoples like the Indonesians. In other situations linguistic separation is encouraged by the creation of an artificial language based on one group of dialects in a larger whole. Such has been the development of Macedonian Slavic whose divergence from standard literary Serbian and Bulgarian was artificially encouraged. The Soviets have made a real effort to separate the closely related Turkic dialects of Central Asia by diversifying their vocabularies and grammatical features. All of these are cases in which languages, old or new, are used as anchors for some kind of national identity; we might also cite Hebrew in the State of Israel, Erse in the Irish Republic, and Afrikaans in Dutch (Boer) areas of South Africa.

One of the keys to social intercourse is the extent and relative geographic position of territories in which any particular idiom is current. This is an index to the range in space of the social relations dependent on a given tongue. Upon mutual intelligibility through a common speech or the more laborious way of translation depends the organization of production and exchange. These activities in turn contribute much to modification of environment. The scale and scope of human undertakings are expressed in the degree of modification and themselves tend to reflect the size of the communicating group. The social world of the monolingual Totonac of Oaxaca in Mexico or of the Arapesh of southeast New Guinea is circumscribed partly because of linguistic isolation. The social universe of the Englishman is shared, however, not only with residents of the United States and the Commonwealth countries, but also with English-speaking educated Parsees, Japanese, Hottentots, and Samoans. There are infinitely more possible contacts with other people open to an English-speaker than to a Totonac-speaker, more accessible social arrangements, more places he can go. The implication for environment is clear. Whereas the Totonac, for example, work alone and so can change their environment only slowly and slightly, Englishmen participate in a great national economy that has changed the face of their country and that has promoted transformations in other countries all over the world. Linguistic isolation necessarily precludes participation for the Totonac even in the larger Mexican economy except as a poorly paid common laborer. Linguistic factors such as these do not alone determine the size or effectiveness of undertakings, of course, but they can impose limits upon them.

The number of distinct linguistic groups in a given area, therefore, can tell us something about the cultural and economic contacts of that area. A region having many small separate language communities is almost by definition a backward region, but not always: Switzerland is thus. The map of such units shows the highest density in those same "linguistic museums" previously mentioned, and only somewhat lower densities in other parts of the "remote" areas of the world.

The geographic patterns of bilingualism and multilingualism are also significant for their effect on the degree of inter-societal integration which is possible. In some parts of the world bilingualism is extremely common. Thus many speakers of isolated North Caucasian languages, some of which are used only by a few hundreds of people in one or two *auls,* turn to Kumyk (a

Turkic dialect), Arabic, or Russian as a medium of intercourse with their neighbors. Some of the Indians of Mexico communicate with other Indians and *mestizos* in Spanish. English is used in India as a language of the intellectuals. The peyote ceremonies of North American Indian tribes, attended by members of many different groups, are largely in English.

There is some variation as to the number and nature of the people in a society who speak the lingua franca. Adult males who have served in the Russian, Mexican, or Indian army go back to their villages speaking some Russian, Spanish, Hindi, or English, respectively. For generations, speakers of national languages have filtered back into the dialect-using villages of France, Germany and other European countries from the armies. Their presence has helped to extinguish local dialects altogether. Thus, bilingualism is often a consequence of the contact of adult males with the outside world through military service, trade, or trips to engage in work, and in some cases it also becomes established through schooling. Women are likely to lag behind in learning an outside language (except that, as someone put it, "prostitutes are the world's best practical linguists"). Sometimes only a scribe, mullah, or village secretary knows the lingua franca. The relative proportion within the more restricted speech groups of persons knowing a widely current tongue is a matter of some importance for the ability of that group to enter into wider geographic relations and for the play of outside influences on the local environment.

KINSHIP AND TRADITION

LANGUAGE has been taken as an index of social integration, which in turn affects the scope and character of human influence on a particular environment. There are mechanisms present among most vertebrates that serve to integrate groups, that is, to define, stabilize, and mediate the relations among individuals, both of the same and of different species. Among mammals, the interspecific relationships of predators to prey and the subsisting order of deference and avoidance among species (biological

rank), as well as intraspecific social rank, are means of integration. Another such means is the mechanism of territorial behavior.
Reproduction and the activities involved in the construction of
dwellings and the care of the young that sometimes accompany
reproductive pairing are other forms of social integration.

Human beings possess the usual mammalian social mechanisms.[7] The reproductive union in man, though it takes many
particular forms, almost always implies the formation of a family
unit with its own household and provisions for the care and
nurture of the young. One of the universal and fundamental
traits that set human societies apart, though, as Kroeber has
pointed out, is the recognition of kinship relations.[8] Kinship,
based entirely on some assumptions about descent, variously
construed, forms a cornerstone of human societies. A great part
of the behavior of persons in any society toward their fellows is
controlled by the kinship relations of the respective parties. Many
societies assign some definite kin status to every human, with
respect to a given other human, and expect all their members
to act in accordance with this arrangement. Kinship mechanisms
bring about a stabilization and regularity of behavior; that is,
they integrate groups, whether through the universal incest
taboo, mother-in-law avoidance, blood-brother fealty, adoption,
inheritance, or nepotism. They provide a basis for people's living
together in groups larger than the nuclear family.

A *kinship group* is, therefore, often the basis of a territorial
unit of joint occupance. In certain kinds of societies, notably
the most primitive ones, the territorial and the kinship boundaries
are usually coextensive. Kinship arrangements may result in the
apportionment of adjacent territories to less closely related groups
sharing real or supposed common ancestry, like clan or lineage
partner groups. The entire set of separate small kinship units
may come together at some time of year as among the Australian
native peoples. Sometimes these groups share certain rights in
each others' territories, such as the privilege of gathering wild
honey or sea foods in times of particular abundance.

When a group of more than family size shares a larger territory, increased continuity in the life of the social unit and
opportunity for greater diversity of ideas and habits are intro-

duced. The kin-based society can have a culture. In many mammalian species, the offspring of an isolated nuclear family are
likely to wander off in adolescence or at adulthood, recognizing
no bonds either of kinship or of kind with the parents. Such a
family is not suited to cultural development. But a human group
of several different families and generations, sharing a territory,
can, and always does, possess a continuing and flexible tradition.
Since kinship provides a setting for culture and the symbolic
communication dependent on it, which are the binding elements
in human society, we may say that kinship relations are the first
form of social organization that is distinctively human.

Kinship groups themselves are inconceivable without culture.
Kinship categories are eminently cultural, and thus variable between human groups. They are based upon varying theoretical
outlooks upon the universe by which the relation of one person
to another is explained. The myths that explain the origin of
individuals and of the kin group are likely to refer to far more
than the human members of the group. They may take in animals, plants, and stars as well, and are interlaced with myths
concerning other aspects of the universe. Holding these ideas
in common, the kinship group becomes a community of outlook
and interests, as well as a territorial and population unit.

A corpus of myths and beliefs, like a language, implies a
classification of the phenomena of experience and also suggests
theories of how things happen, what may be good or bad, and
how things are done. Human groups each have their own view
of nature and of its elements and processes, which often include
what we should call supernatural as well as material agencies.
They have prescriptions for dealing with nature, from magical
formulae and ceremonious ritual directed to control of invisible
forces to technical knowledge of the means of dealing with
visible material nature. They also possess ethical and moral codes
relating to the quality of human acts. We are used to thinking
of these as the separate spheres: science, religion, technology,
and morality, but, as Malinowski has shown, it is very hard to
separate these elements in the behavior of a people.

The single term *tradition* perhaps best describes the form in
which these and other related phases of belief and practice

appear in most human societies. The explicit knowledge, assumptions, and rules of procedure in a society are fused into its peculiar tradition. This is another vital mechanism of integration coexisting with and interacting with the kinship system. Tradition is maintained, transmitted, mediated, and modified by particular agencies acting for the benefit of the whole society. It is recorded in folktale, song, riddle and proverb, ritual, and the arts. It is taught in secret societies, through apprenticeship, and in schools. It is modified by the creativity of artistic, inventive, or exploratory individuals; by its borrowings; by the force of circumstances; and by the inertia and forgetfulness of the people.

The social unit held together by common tradition may coincide with the individual territorial group, especially in very primitive societies. More commonly a tradition is to a large degree shared among several territorial groups, united by a common language and by more remote relations of kinship. Small related bands or territorial groups may come together on occasion in tribal gatherings with their kin, who share their tradition. Tradition may indeed be common to much larger groups that include countless small local units, forming whole nations or even larger entities. Relative unity of tradition sometimes transcends major linguistic boundaries.

The geographic effect of social integration based upon common tradition is greater than that of territorial patterns based upon kinship.[10] A tradition provides a basis for social interaction of wider scope, resting upon agreement among individuals and groups as to principles of ultimate appeal, supreme sanctions, common denominators of value. For some parts of the world today, nevertheless, kinship territories are still significant geographic units. They appear still in native Australia, Melanesia, parts of Africa, the Indian areas of the Americas, a few spots in India, and so on, but even in these places, the limits of social interaction are not so frequently set by kinship as in the past. Over most of the world, however, kinship continues to play an important role in social relationships, especially in very local contexts.

The kin-based social order is seldom dominant. In the more

populous and advanced countries, quite different systems replace it as the chief basis of integration. The dichotomy between local, kin-based traditional social orders and others is expressed in the distinctions made between *Gesellschaft* and *Gemeinschaft* by Tönnies; in Redfield's "folk-urban continuum"; in Maine's differentiation between "status" and "contract" relations; in the difference between "open" and "closed" communities noted by many sociologists.[11] The local communities defined by unique language and tradition and by setting themselves apart as separate kin-universes in their own territories are all small numerically and in the area they occupy. By their nature they are little involved in the doings of others. Geographically, the other kinds of communities that are less exclusive are vastly more important.

The integration of social action through common tradition reaches beyond the borders even of linguistic units, especially where what Redfield calls a "great tradition" holds sway,[12] as in the realms of Islam, in China, in India, and in "the West." A great "world language" or lingua franca is almost always the vehicle of a great tradition. The sharing of such a great tradition is always a matter of degree; some members of a given society are fully absorbed in the stream of it, others are marginal to it or oblivious of it. Alongside the intellectuals,—the mullahs and cadis, the mandarins, the brahmins, the churchmen, poets and professors—dwell the untouched common folk, immersed in their own "little tradition," worshiping local gods and natural forces, casting spells, practicing folk-arts, and preferring ancient ways. Even in the United States, the anti-intellectualism and the isolationism sometimes alleged to characterize the people are nothing out of the ordinary, but only an expression of the abiding attachment to the local and the familiar which is the soul of the "little tradition."[13] In some places, though, the attachment of the few to the exotic, cosmopolitan and unfamiliar themes of the great tradition produces a group in the population that is at home in neither world, the intelligentsia. Intelligentsias have been the spearhead of change, of penetration by the mechanisms of more widespread intersocietal integration, in the more "backward" countries. They enjoy great power and privilege today in such places as Latin America, native Africa, India, the Far East and the Arab world, as well as in Eastern Europe. In all of these regions, the older traditions are being challenged by the essentially Western one that America and Russia share.

The distribution of present-day cultural traditions shows, therefore, not only the results of historic processes of contact and diffusion, conquest and domination, but also the main communities of interaction. There are at least five major categories of populations, with their respective territories, in this regard: 1) the small self-contained communities in which kinship, language, and tradition are held exclusively by a single group which is bound closely together apart from the rest of the world; 2) the major existing communities of "great tradition," including on occasion a large number of different language groups and overriding kin differences; 3) the modern cosmopolitan order, reaching out to unite all the world, halting at no borders, but not yet paramount; and 4) the societies in rapid transition from the first to the second, and 5) from the second to the third condition. Such a classification as the foregoing is simply a statement of the general fact that populations, with their territories, proceed from lesser to greater involvement in the wider world, and from isolation to incorporation in large systems. The process of integration takes place at different rates and even in different directions, and sometimes local groups may retrogress to isolation as did the Maya of Quintana Roo described by Redfield.[14] On the whole, however, advancing integration is a reality. The actual process, or rather the manifold processes, involved are very complex, and the resultant circumstances are very diverse at any moment, so anything asserted about these matters is an oversimplification.

Kinship and culture, including language and tradition, thus serve to integrate societies, both internally and in some degree with their neighbors. Any human community is knit together by land and lore, by love or law. It is also held together by virtue of other characteristics equally well based in man's mammalian nature, including the apportionment of power among community members and the effects of this upon rank and territorial behavior.

RANK AND TERRITORY

IT IS SIGNIFICANT that we use such originally spatial terms as "social position," "social distance," and "mobility," in talking about societies, for the social order is always closely correlated with particular spatial arrangements. This is true of many animals besides man. The close connection between social and spatial arrangements among men may become more easily intelligible if we consider first the general relationships of rank and territory among animals.

The territory within which an animal lives is almost always shared with animals of other species and with other members of its own species. There is, therefore, some considerable overlap in the demands placed upon the territory and its resources by the various creatures inhabiting it, and some competition in the use of sites and substances of the habitat. The conflicts of this kind that occur between individuals in a given habitat are not typically resolved by violent encounters; more commonly one individual acquiesces, giving up priority in the use of places and resources. There is much more deference and surrender than open warfare among animals, though the order or precedence among species, and among individuals within species, rests ultimately upon the actual or potential use of force. These relationships that allocate prerogatives in a regular order among species and within species are known as *rank*.[15]

Biological rank is the name given to the order of precedence among different species that governs the respective roles of their members in an encounter.[16] The hyena cedes place to the lion, the deer shrinks away from the elk, the crow withdraws before the vulture, and almost all beasts flee the presence of man. This order of deference is not a matter of the predator-prey relationship as such, but rather of a recognition of the power of the individual of the dominant species to impose its will and to secure its claim upon any privilege that both desire. Biological rank appears to depend rather closely upon relative fighting ability, but few cases are reported of violent encounters between members of different wild species over booty; a snarl, a look, even the mere presence of the dominant animal is enough to provoke the prudent withdrawal of the weaker one.

Biological rank grades into the violent relationships of predation, on the one side, and on the other approximates a social relation, which provides stability and order in the community with a minimum of outright violence among species. Man is almost always the most feared and privileged member of the company.

Within a single-species population there are two kinds of territorial arrangements: 1) the separate and exclusive occupation of contiguous territories by single animals or by mating pairs and their young, and 2) the joint occupation by a group composed of many individuals of various descent.[17] These two possible arrangements are not necessarily mutually exclusive in a given species. The assignment of territories to individual males may occur, as among some birds, only for the duration of the courtship and mating period, after which the group harmoniously shares a single undivided territory. Exclusive territorial rights may be maintained, also, for only a small part of the territory used by an individual, and the rest may be shared; many animals defend their exclusive individual claims to the "home range" where the dwelling is, but forage in the company of their fellows in a common feeding territory.

Within a species, there is commonly a regular order of precedence similar to that among different species, known as *social rank*.[18] The most striking demonstraton of this system is the "peck-order" shown by Schjelderup-Ebbe to exist among chickens and other birds. There is normally a gradation of privilege and what might be called prestige, based upon combative success and enforced by threats where necessary, among a great many kinds of animals and also among men. Social rank is not always a straight line relationship: individual "A" may dominate "B," and "B" dominate "C," but on occassion "C" may dominate "A." This does not detract from the effect of social rank as a regulator of behavior in individual encounters, however.

Social rank is linked with territory. Almost any individual, in many species, is dominant within its own home territory, though he may be "at the bottom of the heap" outside it. Each particular hierarchy of ranked individuals, too, corresponds to a given specific population in a definite common territory, and any individual of the species introduced from outside must fight his way into the social order or be cast out or killed.

Biological and social rank and territorial behavior are as characteristic of man as of other vertebrate animals. Social rank is another of the powerful integrating mechanisms of human groups. Kinship position itself confers rank, tradition reinforces it, language expresses it. Among most adult humans within a ranked group there are seldom direct physical encounters to decide precedence of rank, but conflicts of interest are resolved among both men and animals by invoking rank and implied power.

Human societies are ranked systems in which not only individuals but large groups are assigned places in the order of precedence. These groups are often internally arranged by rank. Human societies, in other words, are often stratified into classes, castes, estates and other divisions. The assignment of rank to an individual within a social stratum, or to one stratum relative to another, does not normally depend upon the open use of force. There are other and subtler means of advancing claims to rank through what is called *political action*.

Political relations, as the term is intended here, are established in encounters where the direct exercise of force is held in abeyance, usually because some social agency monopolizes the predominant means of forcible action. *Politics* consists of the mutual assessment by interested parties of one another's ability to muster support for their respective opinions, and of the making of joint decisions in accordance with these judgments. The shadow of power always lurks behind political decision and the compliance it demands.

The *social order* is the ranking of social groups; it is enforced not only by kinship and tradition, but often by a legal structure that is the result of past political action. Social stratification is often changed gradually by means of legislative action. When ordinary political devices are abandoned in favor of the use of force to change the social order, we speak of *revolution*. Normally, though, the legislative political functions in a society assign rank and role to individuals and groups. The daily behavior of the individual and groups is regulated by the legal and the administrative structure, respectively. The legal establishes patterns for the solution of conflicts among individuals and groups. The administrative structures direct their cooperation. The political order usually embraces the whole society, whether the political functions reside in particular formal institutions or are embedded informally in other units of organization.[19]

Besides the explicitly political order that permeates the whole society, there are countless other ways in which political action substitutes for forcible action in regulating the relations among individuals and groups. "Politicking" is a form of behavior almost universal in its scope, an indispensable regulatory device. Political relations, having for their object the non-violent adjudication of differences, the establishment of ranking, and the making and enforcement of decisions in a group, are an extension of relations determined by tradition and by the emotions attaching to kinsfolk and familiar associates.[20] In relations among individuals there are positive incentives, as well as negative sanctions that enter into political and other decisions; kindness, empathy, compassion, loyalty and solidarity are at least as characteristic determinants of human action as is the implication of force. Likewise, the relations of individuals to larger groups are governed by such motives as the sense of altruism, fair-play, honesty, dedication and patriotism as well as by power.

Political functions are essential to a society. Many societies otherwise united by language, tradition and sometimes by kinship also depend upon specific political institutions for their integration; in all, there reside some political functions. Political organization may either coincide with these other features of societal organization or go beyond them.

Political organization and political action have always a territorial basis. The group participating in and governed by decisions under a particular institution is defined by territorial limits. The interaction between groups and individuals inhabiting different territories where different political systems hold sway may also be regulated by political action. However, between the folk of different political and territorial units force is often employed in settlement of conflicts over material interests or over intergroup rank. "War is the extension of politics" between groups. Where no permanent accepted organs of political procedure are available to regulate relations among several different territorial, social, and political entities, war becomes a means of arriving at decisions. In some parts of the world intergroup relations are still almost entirely on a basis of permanent enmity. Even in the so-called advanced countries, the techniques of warfare have progressed farther and faster than have the techniques of peaceful political interaction among nations, so that war is a still greater threat to humanity in powerful industrial countries in close, mistrustful contact with each other.

The geographical expression of human territoriality and ranking is most striking in the division of the world into units of political organization, each sovereign and capable both of peaceable and of warlike interaction. All of the territories of the earth are under some form of state sovereignty. We may recognize among politically organized territories the following kinds.

1. First there are the *national states*. These are territories having populations of common tradition and language. Often the national states embrace within their borders even minorities that have a tradition of their own rooted in distinct language, religion, or history. The prototypal and still most typical of national states, like France and England, possess substantial national minorities. In the Soviet Union, the national minorities have been accorded the status of autonomous nationalities within the all-embracing Soviet nationality. They are allowed to maintain their languages and some other elements of cultural distinctiveness, while being incorporated firmly into the political and social framework of the Communist state.

2. A second category of politically organized territories is the *alien dependency*. These entities are very diverse, falling into three different classes.

a. First, are the areas pre-empted from their earlier inhabitants and settled predominantly by immigrants. These are per-

haps best called true "colonies." They are exemplified by French
Canada, the United States, Australia and New Zealand, Argentina, Manchuria, Siberia proper, Canada and Israel. All of these
have been colonized by one or more "metropolitan countries."
Often the colonies have in time chosen to sever their formal ties
with the motherlands, and have opened their borders to the
immigration of peoples other than the original settler group.
They usually manifest a continuing unity of tradition with the
countries of their origin.

b. A second class of alien dependencies is the territory seized
and ruled, but little settled by the people of the controlling
power. Some of these countries are used for the specialized
production of certain goods, and may be thought of as primarily
investment areas. Such are the tropical lands in which few
people from European mother countries settle, but where valuable commodities like sugar, coffee, tea, spices, vegetable oils,
fibres, and minerals are produced for market under enterprises
managed by the outsiders, and often operated mainly by imported laborers. The tropical plantation dependencies of Western
European countries were the scene of early forms of true capi-
talist production, dependent upon metropolitan investors for
supervision and supply, and on coolies for labor. Such places
as the West Indies, Ceylon, Java, the Philippines, Mauritius,
and Reunion are or have been dependencies in this sense. In
some such places the original population has disappeared, as in
the West Indies; or unpopulated islands have been settled by
folk imported to labor on them, like Mauritius; or both things
have occurred, and mixed populations from everywhere like
those of Trinidad, Hawaii, Tahiti, or Natal occur. Some of the
tropical investment dependencies have been marginal to large
areas, still inhabited by thriving native populations, and not used
by the outsiders. These occur in the Philippines, West Africa,
and Indonesia. Another sort of investment area is the mining
country, which in earlier times was often a nucleus of foreign settlement and of labor immigration. Mexico and Peru are heritors
of this kind of dependent regime blended with other types.

Of course investment is not always dependent upon political
control, and foreign enterprise often continues to function when

the political ties with the dependencies are severed. This frequently happens now. The turnover of power by a colonial power to a local regime often means that a new national state becomes established around one tribe or nation within a former dependent territory inhabited by many very unlike and inimical groups. The half-Westernized local intelligentsia, usually drawn from only a few favored peoples and strata of the population, comes to power over large territories in which the former colonial rule held sway, without necessarily representing more than a minute fraction of the populace. After colonial rule conditions never seem to return to the *status quo ante.*

c. A third kind of dependency is the purely *commercial* one, where a foreign power has stepped in to promote order and to enhance the attractiveness of a territory as an investment area or market for the goods and services of the metropolitan country. India was the best example of such a dependency. Nicaragua and Haiti were so occupied, temporarily, by the United States. In the long run, all three types of dependency relations are likely to occur together in different proportions within a territory, and the conditions introduced by colonial rule continue beyond independence. The link with a more cosmopolitan cultural tradition subsists, and Pakistanis go on speaking English, wearing plaid kilts, and wheezing bagpipes; elite Tunisians continue speaking French and sipping apperitifs after they are free. So also do the established commercial and investment activities continue under almost the same arrangements in some cases. And so does the skeleton of territorial jurisdiction remain, the same territories being under new rulers who are sometimes still practically alien to most of the population. The outlines of colonial territories, established without much regard for the ethnic complexities of the country, remain after the overlords are gone, so that there is a Ghana or a Nigeria with little true national foundation. Sometimes the administrative divisions of former great empires have persisted as separate countries, as in Hispanic America, where old provinces became independent states. Dependencies may also split up at independence, as did India and Indo-China.

3. A third category of political units is the type of closed

and autonomous communities based on kinship, common language and tradition that lie within the spheres claimed by various national states. Of this kind are a multitude of local polities in New Guinea, Indonesia, Peru, Bolivia, Brazil, Mexico, Guatemala, Laos, India, Ethiopia, the Sudan, and so on.

The internal spatial structure as well as the extent and position of these three kinds of political units are significant. Most such units are built around what Mark Jefferson and Derwent Whittlesey called an "ecumene," that is, a core of densest settlement and most abundant transportation facilities.[21] This feature is especially well marked in some places in Latin America, where a populous central zone is sometimes joined within a state to a great, almost empty hinterland.[22] The concentration of formal political institutions in particular spots is also both a practical necessity and an important influence in the life of a political unit. Centers of power of this sort are most often in the largest cities of a modern country, where a variety of services and amenities is available to the political leadership, and where growth is probably much stimulated by their political functions. Cities have, since their earliest appearance, been associated with extended political relations in a dependent countryside.

One of the chief features of political organization of territory is its hierarchical nature. Political entities are grouped on the basis of territorial proximity into larger unions subject to the authority of superior agencies, with a regular increase in degree of authority and scope of territorial jurisdiction up to the supreme national authority. The nature of the association may be either central, in which the highest agency reserves all power and delegates it to subsidiary political units of lesser territorial jurisdiction; or federal, in which entities with sovereign powers delegate some of these powers for common purposes to a central agency.

SOCIAL INTEGRATION:

A SUMMARY

WE HAVE NOW SEEN how human societies are bound together, and how human beings in societies can act and live together through the use of certain integrating mechanisms. Out of the general mammalian reproductive union develops the human bond of kinship, and the residential agglomerations built around it are cemented further by language and tradition, which at length permit of human social organizations transcending the boundaries of real or fictive kinship. The kin group and its more extensive successors are associated with a given territory.

The territorial and ranking habits of mammals appear in very complex form in human behavior, especially in the political regulation of interpersonal and intergroup relations and in warfare. We have seen how, through various mechanisms, the several human groups are constituted and have taken note briefly of how they are distributed about the world. Unfortunately, too little is known at present of the size, composition, and location of human social and linguistic groups to justify an attempt to present these subjects cartographically; the results of such an attempt would be sketchy and even misleading for many areas of the world.

Now we shall consider how further integration is achieved within human societies through the mutualistic symbiosis of economic life. In the ensuing chapters, we shall discuss the economic and technical arrangements that obtain within and among societies organized upon the principles that have been described.

The effect of ranking and territoriality is to restrict the geographic impact and expression of any particular culture and economy to specific areas, and so to produce a mosaic of various distinctive "cultural landscapes." Cultural differences in ways of comprehending and modifying environments tend to accompany the division of humanity into the various kinds of groups described. Even within one socio-territorial unit, however, particular economic mechanisms contribute to a further differentiation of the activity that modifies environment. Economic arrangements regulate the location, kind, and amount of modification produced by individuals within the social group, and the interchange and mutual effects between the activities of different groups.

THE ECONOMIC BOND

THE FORMS of economic organization and the substantive processes of economic life in a society are, from our standpoint, means of exploiting and of compensating for the uneven distribution of natural features in space, and their variation in time.

THE PROBLEM OF LIVELIHOOD

THE PHYSICAL DIFFERENTIATION of the earth's surface is visibly expressed in the respective distribution of land and water surfaces seen on any map, and in the shape, size and position of irregularities in the solid surface or lithosphere. There are visible differences from place to place in features of vegetation and in animal life, and these reflect in turn the characteristic states of the atmosphere and the regime of water supply. All of these in turn, with the composition of the rocks, influence the variation of the soil.

The major distributional patterns of these features, and their seasonal and secular variations, are the concern of physical geography. It is the minor and local patterns of distribution, and their variation over shorter ranges of time, however, that are of most consequence to individual human groups. As physical geography regards the surface features of the earth, they fall into various discrete categories, each of which may be studied separately. Such are the landforms considered by geomorphology, the weather sequences of climatology, or soils; as men meet and use these features, they are always fused inseparably into a distinctive local complex. Physical geographers see these features varying gradually over space and slowly through time, but practical humans must classify them functionally, according to the outlook and wants of each human group, and must take account of differences that are of direct significance to man. We can look at nature in this context as "natural resources." The features of most concern, then, are such things as the presence in a vegetation of plants useful for human purposes, and their seasonal regime; the location, abundance, and habits of usable animal species; the occurrence of useful mineral substances; the presence of suitable sources of potable water; the lay of the land as it affects shelter, communication, and defense; the relative harshness of immediate surface climate, as registered in human physiology; and the climate, water supply, soil and biota as they affect the growth of edible and other useful plants. These features of environment, seen in terms of human ends and interpreted through a particular culture are, very broadly speaking, *natural resources*.

We have seen that for a stationary plant the immediate natural conditions of its growing site are all-important, but that a mobile animal circulates about its habitat and selects the appropriate locale for each of its activities. We may say, therefore, that the uneven distribution of natural resources in space and time is a decisive influence on the behavior of any of the higher terrestrial mammals, including man. The location of particular surface features of consequence to the individual, as well as the qualitative and quantitative properties of the resource as the animal or human individual utilizes it over time, are significant.

Of importance are not only the location, abundance, and accessibility of a food plant or game species, for instance, but also its recuperative and reproductive capacity under any given intensity of harvesting or predation. Similarly not only the fertility of a soil, but also its susceptibility to surface washing and the rate of its replenishment of nutrients are significant for its user.

The animal harvests or preys; it garners a livelihood from sites it knows, and its part in modifying the environment is a consequence of this activity. The effects produced by animals on the environment condition its capacity to support them, and so their interaction with the environment tends to be self-limiting. Animals dwelling and moving within a restricted range of territory and depending on limited resources may, if they disturb the balance of the habitat and abuse the resources on which they depend, meet with a reduction of their numbers as a consequence. An equilibrium between the population and its resources is thus approached.

The livelihood of men and other beings ultimately depends on the natural conditions of the habitat. These natural conditions are affected by the work of man himself as part of nature, and his livelihood thus depends to a marked degree upon his own activity. Human economies differ as to the scale at which they organize the processes that furnish man his livelihood. The greater the scope of organized co-operation, the larger, in general, can be the effect of human intervention in nature. As the degree of human intervention in the complex interactions of the habitat increases, direct dependence for food supply and other needs upon the seasonal cycles of plant and animal life decreases, and increasingly foresighted human efforts add further utility to natural products.

Through ingenuity and effort, man's technical and economic institutions mediate between the raw environment and human life, but this less immediate dependency is only complementary, not opposite, to ultimate dependence upon nature. The strategy that so releases man from simple and immediate dependence upon the moods of nature rests completely upon planned and organized behavior. The price of liberation from direct dependence on the natural environment is subjection to societal regulation.[1]

THE ECONOMY

AS THE FOREGOING PAGES show, man is a genuinely social animal, and human economic life is socially regulated. The old idea of a primitive egoistic state of "individual economy" that appears in the speculation of early economic writers has been repudiated by Marx, and is now generally abandoned.[2] Because of man's long, vulnerable period of immaturity, his physical decline in old age, his dependence on learned techniques, and because of his need for artifacts (usually made by others) to perform his work, he is scarcely conceivable as other than a social being. He must be able to rely on the group for protection, cooperation, and guidance when necessary.

Human economic life, then, is the affair of organized groups.[3] The mechanism of symbolic communication, and the basis of shared tradition, are characteristic of economic as of other social units, and economic units are arranged according to kinship, social rank, territoriality, and other such discriminants. The group that interacts as an economy, however, is not necessarily coextensive with or structured in the same manner as any other social unit. An *economic unit* is a special social group for which economic decisions are taken and to which they apply.

Economic decisions are those concerning the allocations of "scarce" means to achieve given ends; or, as others would put it, to "maximize welfare." It is clear that this kind of decision need not be taken rationally, though classical economists did postulate "rational" choice; it is also clear that "scarcity" and "welfare" are purely relative concepts.

Polanyi and his collaborators distinguish two different economic functions: the "substantive" ones that regulate the technical processes of livelihood and the roles of individuals therein, and the "formal" ones that govern the apportionment of goods and services for production and consumption.[4] To put it another way, there are two kinds of economic decisions, one relating to the artificial creation of goods and services; the other, to their apportionment among users. These decisions concern respectively the making and maintenance of an artificial human environment, and its use by members of a society, and the two kinds of decisions are made in two different kinds of social units which may or may not coincide in a given case.

The social unit engaging in acquiring and employing the means of production may be called a *firm,* and that acquiring and employing the goods and services of consumption may be designated a *household.*⁵ The two functions, production and consumption, must ultimately be related and tend mutually to influence each other. The agency which governs this relationship and transmits the influences of consumption to production and vice versa is what may be called the *economy.* The economy is a social unit bound together by formal arrangements for economic decision-making, prevailing over a definite territory, and interacting with other kinds of social units. Customarily it is the formal arrangements themselves which are referred to as "the economy."

Economies in this formal sense of arrangements for the making of decisions having to do with the use and circulation of goods may be classified into a number of distinctive types. Several different classifications have been proposed, employing somewhat different criteria. Since, as we shall see, the form of an economy has a great bearing on the life of the social group and on its capacity to create an artificial environment, we shall consider here the problem of classification according to criteria that have been proposed by previous writers, and shall attempt to arrive at a usable classification based upon several of their measures, as well as upon others that offer themselves.

"MAKING A LIVING"
AND "EARNING A LIVING"

AN ESSENTIAL DISTINCTION is made by Max Schmidt between *friendly* and *hostile* economic intercourse.⁶ Predatory and larcenous relations are not uncommon among primitive groups that otherwise sustain little contact among themselves, and these relations can be of considerable importance for the disposition of goods and services. We need not confine this remark to primitives; crime is a similar phenomenon among more advanced peoples and crime, too, is of some considerable economic importance. Hostile economic intercourse may be occasional, periodic, or regularly established. In some cases it takes the form of infrequent raids through the neutral buffer territories that commonly surround an isolated society's lands; in other instances it appears as a yearly tribute or fixed extortion levied by the stronger on the weaker group. Hostile economic relations can mean the total despoilment of the victims, the seizure only of goods of a particular kind, the enslavement of individuals, or even a mere token payment. At last the hostile relation grades away into symbolic affirmations of differential rank among the groups concerned.

Friendly economic intercourse is more usual than hostile intercourse, and forms the basis for sustained and systematic relations governing the production and distribution of goods and services.

Let us recognize two fundamental types of economic systems, those in which a family or individual literally "makes" its own living, and those in which it "earns" its living. The first is what we shall call a *subsistence economy,* the second an *exchange economy.*

We have seen that all human economic life is always in some degree social. That is, at least one social agency is concerned in the economic life of any individual. We noted that the social unit of economic organization is not necessarily coterminous with other social groups, and that affiliations of varying scope are formed for different purposes and by different mechanisms. Among many peoples, the ceremonial and political activity of a community is the affair of a large part of the population, but economic processes are carried on in parallel but separate small household units. Bearing this in mind, we may say that in a *subsistence economy,* a single social unit performs the economic functions relating to production and distribution as well as consumption; and that in an *exchange economy,* more than one social unit is engaged in these functions as they concern any single individual. Within the subsistence system, the small family unit is usually organized as both the unit of production and the unit of consumption, and itself effects the distribution of goods and services among its members. The family unit acts as both household and firm, and therefore also as the economy. All or practically all of the goods produced by its members are consumed by them, and little goes to outsiders; similarly, all of the goods consumed, or almost all of them, are produced within the unit. The individual consumer has usually had some part in the actual production of the goods he uses.[7]

Under an exchange economy goods and services are transferred from one social group to another by one or more of several mechanisms embodied in the larger social unit bound together by the economy, which mediates among these lesser groups. The producers of goods and services exchange them, directly or through intermediaries, with their consumers. They also receive goods for consumption from other producers.[8]

Within the category of exchange economies, a distinction should be made between "closed" and "open" forms. We may call these *price* and *non-price* economies, respectively.[9] In a closed, non-price exchange economy, goods and services are transferred from producers to consumers in accordance with some other principle than equivalence in standard value among the goods themselves. Except for the fact that many different social groups acting in different capacities are involved in its operation, a closed economy of this type is analogous to the subsistence economy of the single household. That is, its operation follows the same principles already present in the subsistence unit, where there is specialization of roles among individuals in the productive process, and a distribution of goods and services among these same individuals in regular but unequal proportions. The closed exchange economy, like the closed individual or subsistence economy, institutes a system of specialized roles in production and consumption among its members, but the consumers of goods and services here are not the same persons as those who produce them.

Specialization, in closed economies, follows lines of age,

sex, descent, and other forms of rank, as well as of skills and particular wants. The organization of economic life makes provision for employment of the strength and endurance of the hardiest or most hapless members of the group in the most demanding tasks, for application of the particular skills of specialists, for the nurture and protection of the young by special means, for the observance of ritual obligations and the reward of high social rank. It is a complex constellation of privileges, exactions, obligations and guarantees binding together the members of the group, laying greater burdens on some than on others, reserving greater rewards and comforts for a favored few. Established relations among persons and among the multitude of lesser social groups regulate the economic functions.

Here we observe an instance of the interrelation of social organization and the economy. The effects of this relationship extend, we shall see, through technique to register upon the environment.

The decisions that govern the allotment of roles to individuals or firms in production, and the allocation of products for consumption, may be made either in a *diffuse* or in a *centralized* fashion. In the *diffuse* case, tradition establishes the mutual rights and obligations of individuals and groups and economic decisions conform to the established principles of status. The role of any individual in productive activity, and his entitlement to consumption rights, are fixed by custom. The amounts and kinds of goods and services produced, too, are a matter of the traditional expectations of the group. The kinds of plants and animals that are gathered, hunted, cultivated, or raised; the tools used; the techniques employed; and the time spent are defined by tradition. What becomes of the product is known in advance, according to the structure of established socio-economic relations. Economic decisions are hardly more than recognitions of the rules of habitual conduct. This form of exchange, which is regulated by the mutual relations traditionally obtaining among persons, is what Karl Polanyi calls *reciprocity*.[10]

In the other *centralized* form of decision-making it is a policy rather than a tradition that regulates economic behavior. In a

centrally directed economy,[11] or as Polanyi calls it, a *redistributive economy*, a single economic agency is paramount and makes
decisions for the whole society. The policy of the redistributive
agency may respond to any conceivable motives of its managers,
and may remain relatively constant or vary in any fashion. Redistribution involves some sort of planning, though not necessarily
prudent or providential planning. It rests upon a stratification
of social groups, expressed in the authority of the few over
the economy of the many, and so implies the presence of an
elite commanding power and privileges far superior to those
of the rest of the society. The function of the dominant group
is to allocate rather than to produce.

In a redistributive economy, central decisions determine
how much shall be produced, or perhaps more commonly, how
much shall be delivered by each firm, and apportion the total
product among the households that are its consumers. Goods
and services produced by one social group are passed on through
the central agency to other groups. The policy of the redistributive agency is independent and all-important. It bears no
necessary or predictable relation to the traditional social relationships in the society it serves, nor does it institute any one
invariable proportion between the kind and volume of production undertaken by a particular group and the nature and
amounts of goods and services that group is entitled to consume.
Redistribution makes possible the allocation of some part of the
total goods and services produced to purposes other than those
of single consumer households. It can dedicate materials and
effort to the furtherance of general social ends, or to the private
gratification of the small group that dominates the economy.[12]
It can set aside goods for investment, or accumulate them as
safeguard against emergencies. It can employ its command of
economic power to enforce guarantees of public order and security in the society.

Redistribution is a necessary condition and an essential
feature of government, and governments always exercise a redistributive function. There is some similarity between the
hostile economic intercourse discussed earlier and the redistributive relation, for both depend upon the employment or potential

threat of force, The redistributive function specifically depends, however, upon a monopoly of force, and on an institutional relation established within a society. The regular and exclusive use of redistributive power by an agency organic to a given society is quite different from raids by enemies and the activity of criminals, and governments make every effort to suppress competition from this quarter.[13] Authentic redistributive agencies often invoke as much violence, however, and show as little respect for individual "rights" and interests, as do criminals and predatory raiders. Under both types of economy, goods and services are transferred not in return for goods and services of equal value—there may be no concept of equal value in these cases—but in accordance with the specific obligations of one person toward another, of an individual toward the redistributive state or collectivity, of the collectivity in turn toward individuals.

The third possible kind of exchange is *the market*. In the market system, goods and services are assigned commensurable values according to some common standard, and are exchanged according to equivalence in these values, or prices.[14]

If there are numerous different and incommensurable standards of value for different kinds of goods, the exchange is of the *barter* type, which is incompletely subject to market principles. In barter, there are no universal media of exchange. Under a barter system, a cow may be exchanged against wheat, in kind, but its value may not be convertible directly into a given amount of silver or a definite assortment of iron tools. A "bride-price" may prescribe the exchange of a specific kind of goods in a definite amount for the right of marriage. Land or labor may not be subject to exchange at all under the barter system, and some sort of communal landholding or joint working groups may regulate their apportionment.[15] The barter system is suitable for a small volume of trade in a few standard items, and often has appeared as the form of economic intercourse between peoples of very different culture and techniques, but it is not well suited to the task of organizing economic relations within a non-subsistence society.

In a full market economy, economic relations are "open"

from the standpoint of society. No particular pre-existing condition either of personal status or of state policy fully controls the manner in which an individual or group may dispose of or acquire goods. Any producer may exchange his product for other goods of equal price, and any consumer may acquire goods equivalent in value to what he has to offer. No special agency exists to govern exchange. The market itself, which may either consist of actual "crowds" of buyers and sellers or may have no corporeal existence, establishes relations between supply and demand that are symbolized by price and that set the conditions of exchanges.

With the introduction of the term *market*, we must recognize its application not only to the relation of producers with ultimate consumers but also of producers to other producers. Supply and demand relationships affect the space, raw materials, and utilities, the working force, the tools, and plant that are used in production. There may be markets for land, labor, and capital as well as for consumers' goods. A market economy tends to allow the free flow of these so-called factors of production in response to price, as well as to permit of an adjustment of the supply of finished products to the corresponding consumer (or producer) demand at a price reflecting the prices of production factors in their turn. The market, by introducing prices in a single medium for all goods and services, establishes the possibility of direct comparison of one use of an object, or one way of working, with others, and of choice according to considerations of greatest advantage. It also introduces the possibility of competition among firms to produce goods and services at the lowest possible price and to sell them to consumers at the highest possible price.

A barter exchange does not perform the same function as does a full market. It can indeed effect the transfer of goods and services, substantively, but provides no basis for either the determination of comparative advantage in the use of resources and labor, or the competitive relation among firms. It lacks a full formal mechanism to regulate the economy, though it may be associated with trading activity in a crowded marketplace.

In actual fact, the market mechanism is not often, if ever,

perfectly competitive or completely self-regulating. The fore-going classification has deliberately disregarded this fact and other purely empirical considerations. Therefore, while the classification may be both exhaustive and accurate, insofar as it concerns possible ways of discharging the economic functions, it necessarily lacks particularity.[16] We have only to reflect that government, which is clearly redistributive in character, exists in market societies and is in fact indispensable to them, in order to become aware of the differences between the ideal economies here considered and those of the "real world." Several different economic arrangements can and usually do coexist in one society. Actual economies do, however, always consist of relations instituted on the basis of the principles discussed above, and cannot be understood without them.

ECONOMY AS SYMBIOSIS

ALMOST ALL HUMAN BEINGS probably engage at times in some form of exchange. Furthermore, almost all households in exchange economies sometimes engage in production for their own use. From a geographic standpoint, the important distinction to be made is that between the economic system governing the regular and indispensable livelihood activity of a group, and any other systems auxiliary thereto and correspondingly less vital. It is fruitful to think here of the exchange relation as a case of symbiosis. The economy, of course, involves only members of a single species. In Chapter 2 we discussed two kinds of symbiosis—*obligate,* in which the symbiotic relation is essential to the survival of an organism, and *facultative,* in which the organism may take advantage of a symbiotic relationship, but may survive without it quite as well.

The livelihood activities indispensable for the survival of a human group are, roughly, those concerned with the supply of food, water, and shelter. These activities are dedicated to procuring essential non-durable goods. A human economic unit is therefore an obligate symbiosis when its function is to govern the production, distribution and consumption of such essential non-durables as food. On the other hand, the economic unit devoted to procuring durable goods like tools, permanent shelters, and the like, as well as a host of less essential non-durables and luxuries, represents a facultative symbiosis. This distinction is far from precise, but allows us to account for some characteristic combinations of economic systems found empirically. We must leave out of consideration altogether many of the services performed by one individual or group for another, such as ceremonial acts and military campaigns, since these are always implicated in the very constitution of the group, and are not directly under economic control. We recognize, in addition, that the dichotomy between durable and non-durable goods corresponds only in a very imperfect way with the realities of human wants.

Sombart regards everything between subsistence and market economies as *transitional economies*.[17] It is probable that only such transitional, or rather complex economies embodying several different principles of formal economic organization, actually exist; and that there are virtually no human groups which subsist alone with no exchange at all with outsiders; and also no human groups for which the market, without redistributive government or status-oriented reciprocity, controls all the livelihood processes. It is, moreover, extremely doubtful that any pure reciprocal system exists, or that a completely redistributive order can exist beyond the limits of a family or a small village at most.[18]

Considering now the respective obligate and facultative economic forms, the following types suggest themselves:

1) We may think of subsistence economies as obligate forms, augmented only by sporadic facultative recourse to friendly or hostile intercourse with outsiders. A large number of different human communities, with a variety of technical capacities, may be classified in this way as we shall see. In these communities, household and firm are identical, and may be composed of a single nuclear family, with an alternative form of economic organization for the occasional war or trading party.

2) Subsistence economies combined with facultative ar-

rangements for peaceful reciprocal exchange are extremely common in some parts of the world. If the reciprocal exchange may be called "facultative" from the standpoint of livelihood, it is nevertheless anything but unimportant, for it expresses and tends to perpetuate societal bonds, and to carry ceremonial meanings of the utmost significance to those who participate in it. In the societies in which reciprocal exchange is characteristic, its economic character and relation to livelihood are in the shadow of its ritual significance. Economic life in general is intertwined with, and even subordinated to, ceremonial life, as Malinowski has shown.[19]

3) Obligate subsistence may be combined with redistribution. Goods, mostly durable, and services are furnished by the facultative redistribution mechanism, and the supply of primary necessities remains on a subsistence basis. This is one of the two types of peasant economies, and corresponds to the arrangement under which peasants live in a feudal order, or in such redistributive systems as the ancient empires and the transitional socialist states.

4) Obligate subsistence with facultative market relations characterize the second type of peasant economy. The peasant produces most of the food for his own household, as well as other goods commensurate with local technology and resources, and trades for some few but important items.

5) Redistributive and market mechanisms may, and perhaps always do, appear together. Either redistribution or the market may be the obligate form, the other being facultative. There is a wide range of possibilities between these two extremes, and in commercial countries today, both of the "free enterprise" and "Communist" camps, the degree of redistributive intervention is an aspect of policy often discussed. The Soviets open the way only cautiously for private trading of kolkhoz surpluses, and the Americans proceed gingerly to experiment with government enterprise in such matters as electric power development.

The last three cases can serve as illustration for an important principle. This is that the respective degrees of obligate and facultative economic dependence will vary from individual to individual in a complex society. The medieval peasant could

feed himself, even without the services of craftsmen and ad-
ministrators and soldiers; his obligate relation was to the small
group that helped to produce his livelihood. The lord of the
manor and his retinue, however, were utterly dependent upon
the redistributive system that insured them a claim upon the
peasant's product. Perhaps the adscription of the serfs to the
land, and the firm binding of them into the manorial system,
speak for this. In modern peasant countries, the peasants are
not nearly so dependent on the market or the state distribution
agencies as are the folk of the cities.

The five preceding combinations of economic types—simple
subsistence, subsistence with reciprocity, subsistence with redistribution, subsistence with market, and commerce (redistribution with market)—probably best account for the empirical
economies of the present, and for those throughout most of history. It should be remembered, however, that elements of all
the basic arrangements occur within every household. The
reciprocal element of exchange plays a part in all societies, if
for no other reason than that the social discrimination of persons
by age, sex, kinship, and power imposes special rules of interpersonal conduct. Redistribution in the form of taxation and
public expenditure, furthermore, necessarily exists wherever
government exists; and some kind of market, at least in rudimentary form, is necessary wherever planning is not perfect.
Any given act of exchange, in any society, may have to be
classified under any one of the three basic types, or even under
several, depending on its particular circumstances, and any
individual may characteristically depend upon any one of these
forms. The distinction between obligate and facultative forms
is best observed in times of want or danger, and can only be
applied most tentatively in other situations.

With all these limitations on the scheme, however, it is
desirable to recognize these several prevailing types of economies, for the prevalence of one or another of them has much
to do with the livelihood of a society, and so with its relations to the rest of nature, directly and through its artificial
environment.

SPECIALIZATION

ECONOMIC ORGANIZATION and processes were previously identified as means of exploiting and compensating for the uneven distribution of natural resources in space and time. Certain formal types of economies have been considered as they accomplish these things through their effect on the apportionment of products among users. Now the effects of economic organization upon the allocation of goods and services to further productive uses will be considered. Man's distinctive use of tools to make other tools is largely dependent on these effects.

Subsistence is independence; exchange, interdependence. What a subsistence household consumes is what it produces for itself; and what it produces is what the efforts of its own members can make of the resources it commands, using as well as they can the tools and facilities they have been able to provide for themselves. *Subsistence* means getting along without the products of other people's resources, effort and ingenuity; *exchange* means using goods and services produced by others. The exchange relation links up people of different ideas and skills, who exploit varied resources and employ distinctive kinds of tools and facilities, and so contribute a variety of products. It rests upon specialization.

The principle of specialization in exchange appears in the differences among goods and services offered by various producers for consumption, and in the different contributions of individuals to the processes of production. There is some specialization among individuals within the subsistence economy, but it is restricted greatly by the small size of the group, the limited extent of the territory it commands, the great variety of wants its work must satisfy, and the paucity of the equipment it can create and use. Exchange provides a much larger economic unit, which commands a wider territory with more diverse resources, makes place for a high degree of individual and group specialization, and permits the employment of an unlimited variety of material equipment.

One kind of specialization applies to the uses of the natural environment. Usually, a territory offers its possessors at times far more than they can use of some few things, and far less than they want of others. Forest dwellers may hardly touch their timber resource, but be chronically in need of stone for tools; desert peoples suffer from a lack of potable water most of the time, but may have infinitely more stone than they can use. Arctic hunters gorge themselves on meat when they make a kill, and narrowly avoid starvation between successful hunts. Subsistence economy itself offers no solution to this problem, except for whatever the group can do in the way of storing and preserving food and other materials. Exchange makes it possible for the inhabitants of a territory rich in one product to furnish some of their excess to other groups, and to receive in turn some product that they lack but others possess in abundance. There are a multitude of examples of such exchange: such things as flint, obsidian, seashells, metals, and salt, for example, since remote times have been traded over great distances in many parts of the world. There are many instances of exchange of products of the sea for plant foods grown or gathered by inland folk, of wild game for vegetable foods, of highland for lowland products. This specialization of production to take advantage of particular natural environments permits a comparatively thorough utilization of resources and a wider distribution of the benefits therefrom.

Specialization occurs not only in connection with the exploitation of environments, but also in *techniques,* the way in which raw materials are used. Techniques vary even more than natural resources. Several human groups living adjacent to each other may do very different things with the same material endowment; some may be farmers, others gatherers and hunters, others herdsmen, yet others craftsmen. Differences in technique involve four things: 1) the roles taken by particular individuals or groups in production, 2) the equipment used, 3) the kinds and amounts of materials employed, and 4) the places at which particular activities are carried out. Technical specialization expresses essentially a differentiation of artificial environments, as territorial specialization depends upon a differentiation of natural environments. The roles of individuals or groups of humans in work are best classified in terms of the tools and methods that they use, and the quantities of the particular materials used are determined by the same tools and methods. The locations at which work takes place are those at which appropriate tools are present or can be assembled, to which materials can be brought, workers can come, and from which the product can conveniently be moved toward those who will consume it. The location of productive sites in any economy reflects these factors. In an exchange economy, the location of activity responds to particularly complex influences. Technical specialization always conforms to the technical means available; that is, to the particular characteristics, capacities, and locations of the facilities and tools which have already been produced or can be produced. It is governed by the accumulated capital present. This is not to assert, of course, that all of human life is "determined" by technique or capital. Only a portion of human existence is bound up with productive activity, and it takes a certain kind of mystical dogmatism to see the means of production as the master control of human existence, rather than as merely one of its more important limiting factors.

The specialization of production and, just as important, the degree of integration of the special phases of production, in an exchange economy, are dependent on the characteristics of productive capital, that is, on certain features of the artificial environment that a group or groups create. The matter of material technique, and the organization of production in space and time, will be discussed in subsequent chapters. We are concerned here with the ways in which the various forms of economic organization affect production, and through it, consumption.

In a subsistence economy, as we have seen, only a very small social group on limited territory is involved. There is little opportunity for intensive specialization of resource exploitation, though it is usually reported that subsistence groups make good use of such diversity of resources as their natural environment affords. Though such nomadic gatherers as the African Bushmen or the Philippine Aeta know how to find some use for almost every plant or animal in their habitat, and subsistence farming people often know and use hundreds of wild products of the forest as well as what they grow, these groups can utilize the resources of the natural environment only insofar as they fill some want of the group. They have no incentive to gather wild products beyond their own demands. The complexity of production is held to a minimum by the small size of the subsistence group, and nowhere have such groups produced any very elaborate equipment to be used in production. The lack of large and efficient units of productive capital is only partially a consequence of the limitations placed by group size upon specialization. Perhaps even more important as a limiting factor in subsistence production is the lack of regularly instituted contact with outsiders. This situation leads not only to the absence of an exchange of useful tools produced by outside specialists, but as well to the absence of the exchange of ideas and impulses for experiment and innovation. Intellectual as well as material isolation plays its part here.

The incentives to production in a subsistence group are only the wants of the group. There is no thirst for familiar goods from afar to stimulate intensive effort or high ingenuity. The small group's wants, on the other hand, impose a tight discipline on activity. To satisfy these wants with the rude means at their command, subsistence people must attend to their business and not digress from usual patterns to indulge in experiment or idleness. They must be prudent and provident to meet the risks of their isolated life, for they can look to no outside agency for help.

Economies in which reciprocity plays a role are still dominated by the subsistence pattern, but the exchange that takes place along lines of status encourages the production of particular goods connected with ceremonial. The effect of reciprocal exchange is perhaps most marked in the encouragement of specialized artistic production. A high development of plastic arts and ceremonial forms is characteristic of groups, like those of Melanesia and Northwest America, that engage in reciprocal exchange. A certain degree of material prosperity seems to be present where reciprocity occurs, though it is mostly subsistence-based. Indeed, the display of wealth and its pursuit play a major role in these cultures. Perhaps the fruitful gardens and the bounteous schools of fish that sustain these peoples are a necessary precondition for their artistic achievements. Regular intercourse with their neighbors allows these folk access to new ideas, and may have something to do with the considerable development of production techniques found in their societies. Even though exchange does not lead, in this case, to general technical specialization within the society, it no doubt favors the diffusion of ingenious and efficient techniques among different groups; and the imposing artistic productions of some of the societies practicing reciprocity are accompanied by great social differentiation and by considerable densities of population dependent upon the skillful utilization of natural resources.

In *peasant societies* there is a division between the producers of food, who remain on a subsistence basis in regard to basic necessities, and the rest of the population, who are dependent upon them. The rural folk are little specialized in their production, but the urban people are a population of specialists of different kinds. The volume of the peasant's production is not regulated by his own immediate wants alone, but by the wants of the whole society. There are incentives—through exchange—for him to produce as much as possible. The incentives for peasant production vary: under redistribution, quotas for delivery of produce may be imposed upon the peasant; and under the market system, desired goods may be offered to him in exchange for what he produces. Although the volume of production by the peasants is not limited by the peasant's direct wants, it is limited by his lack of specialization. Peasant food production is carried on much as subsistence food production is, with reliance on a diversity of crops and on the versatility of the skills found within the group, as well as with limited means of production. The peasant is much less dependent on the urban folk than they are upon him, and may reject his specialized role as a food producer for the society. Thus, there may result attempts to coerce or entice him into maintaining deliveries.[20]

Redistributive-peasant economies are in quite a different position from *market-peasant economies*. The redistributive economy centralizes and reapportions produce by plan. It works best, probably, where a definite closed system can be maintained with some predictability, and where the various kinds of specializations are in favorable proportion.

The impositions of the redistributive agency on producers may reduce their efficiency if unwisely applied. The exaction of too large a part of the peasant's crop, for example, may deprive him of seed for the next year's sowing, may decrease his physical efficiency through malnutrition, or may cause him to slacken his work in protest. The redistributive agency must find ways of inducing efficient production. If sufficient land, water, tools, and even credit are not provided to the peasants, production suffers. The demands of the urban populace for sustenance may be more urgently registered in political centers than the needs of food producers, causing an ultimate decline in the production of food. In a market-peasant economy these problems can be solved to a certain extent by the spontaneous adjustment of supply and demand; but under redistribution, everything depends upon correct estimates by those in charge of the economy.

The other sector of a peasant economy is the urban. In towns and cities there is always a specialization of individuals in different technical activities, and exchange among them and with the peasants. This specialization may be regulated, again, by either market or redistributive mechanisms. The exchange of finished commodities and services is of course only one part of urban exchange. There is also a great traffic in raw materials, a trade in producers' tools, and a movement of workers among employments. The *factors of production* are allocated either by markets or by planned redistribution, and probably both mechanisms are always present in different proportions. Some exchange of production goods, especially tools, takes place with the peasants for their produce, but throughout most of history the cultivators have employed chiefly their own tools of rustic manufacture.

In mixed peasant-urban societies, the degree of mobility and adaptability of individuals, at least in the urban sector, is high. Intellectual and artistic creativity flourish. In these societies, the cities are centers of innovation, experiment, leisure, and refinement. In the countryside as well as in urban places, high population densities are often attained.

The final kind of system, the fully commercial economy that combines redistributive and market mechanisms, achieves a full exchange relationship in production as well as in consumption. Such an abundant literature on the present and potential standards of welfare, the intellectual interchange, flexibility, mobility, variety and progressiveness of these economies is available that it cannot be even summarized here.

We are dealing with economies having both market and redistributive elements, but which are fully committed to exchange, and in which one or the other regulative mechanism dominates.

One feature distinguishes the predominantly redistributive from the predominantly market economies. This is the degree to which the economy is "open," and therefore can engage in exchange with other economies external to it. The redistributive economy is designed for a specific territory, with a given number of consumers having certain recognized wants, and a given number of producers with certain capabilities and means at their disposal. It establishes overall policies centrally, from which the individual decisions of producers and to some extent even of consumers must follow. It cannot safely plan for what it cannot control, and therefore must remain essentially closed. The economies in which the market is dominant and redistribution is characteristic chiefly of the governmental service functions stand in an "open" relation to other economies, and as long as an outside producer can meet and underbid domestic price terms, he can count on access to the market.[21] The relative economic isolation of the countries behind the

Iron Curtain and their close linkage one with another are at least partially to be understood in terms of their *closed* exchange system.

Despite certain notable differences, however, there are great similarities between countries under *market* and *redistributive* economies today, and an increasing similarity in their productive programs is evident. The differences in organization are clearly a matter of degree, rather than of kind—even between the United States and the Soviet Union—though it is obvious that the degree of difference is vital.

GEOGRAPHY OF ECONOMIC FORMS

SUBSISTENCE WAS, no doubt, the original economic system of mankind. Those areas where subsistence economies hold on today are, because of their exclusion from exchange relations, thought of as backward and remote. Much of the intertropical zone is still outside of commerce. Not only the nomadic hunters and plant gatherers, but many of the farmer folk living in clearings in the forest, back in the hills, and along lonely coasts must be classed as subsistence peoples. Surviving desert hunters like the Bushmen, as well as the remaining Arctic hunting people, live under subsistence economies except where they were caught up in the economy of the intruding Whites. The subsistence economy was practiced widely, though, even in the United States a few generations ago, and is not uncommon among cultivators in Africa, southern Asia, and the New World.

Subsistence with reciprocal exchange is amply documented for the Congo, New Guinea and Melanesia in particular, and formerly was common on the American Northwest Coast and in Australia. Its extension into other subsistence areas is unknown, but it may well occur in Indonesia, Southeastern Asia, and perhaps in the Amazonian interior of Brazil and neighboring countries; regular exchanges of some sort based on intergroup status do occur in some of these regions.

Peasant economies are the most widespread of all at present. Market-peasant relations dominate in most of Europe, the

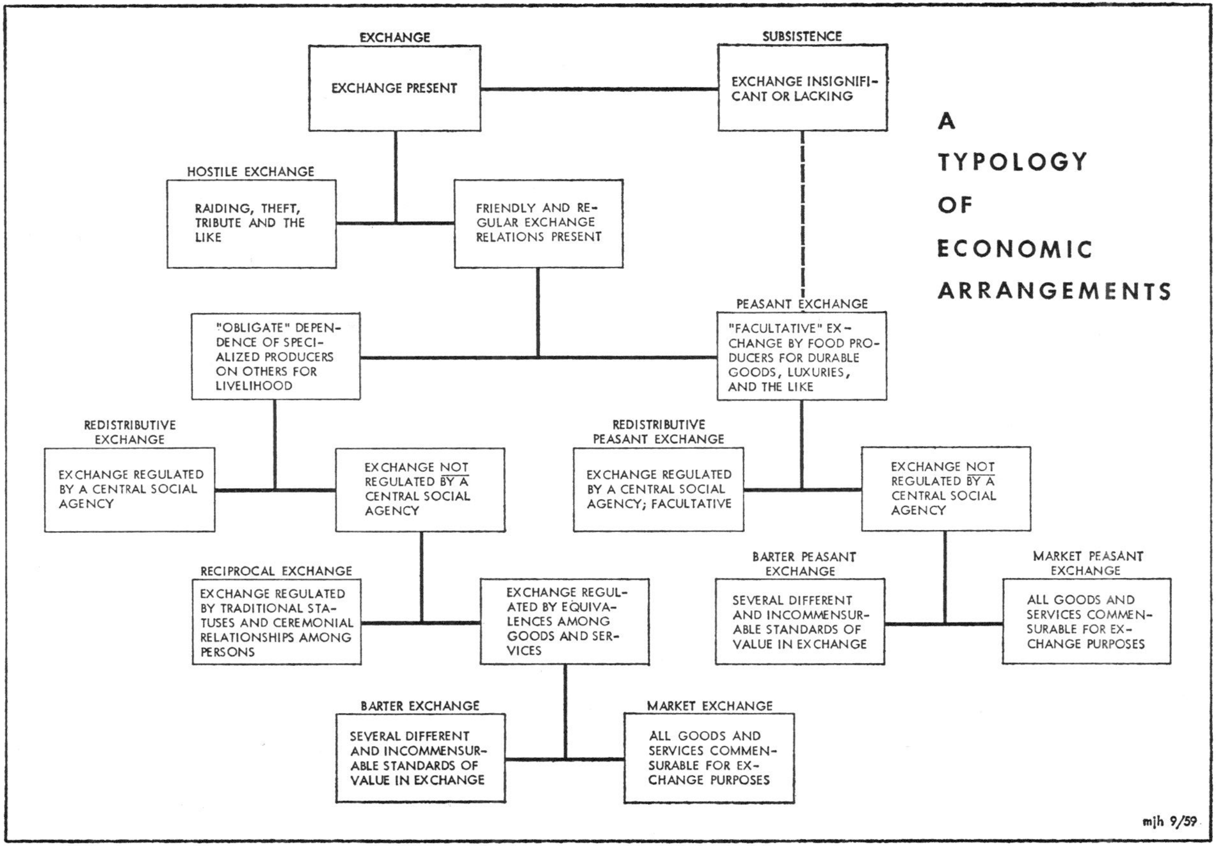

A TYPOLOGY OF ECONOMIC ARRANGEMENTS

EXCHANGE

SUBSISTENCE

EXCHANGE PRESENT

EXCHANGE INSIGNIFICANT OR LACKING

HOSTILE EXCHANGE

RAIDING, THEFT, TRIBUTE AND THE LIKE

FRIENDLY AND REGULAR EXCHANGE RELATIONS PRESENT

"OBLIGATE" DEPENDENCE OF SPECIALIZED PRODUCERS ON OTHERS FOR LIVELIHOOD

REDISTRIBUTIVE EXCHANGE

EXCHANGE REGULATED BY A CENTRAL SOCIAL AGENCY

EXCHANGE NOT REGULATED BY A CENTRAL SOCIAL AGENCY

RECIPROCAL EXCHANGE

EXCHANGE REGULATED BY TRADITIONAL STATUSES AND CEREMONIAL RELATIONSHIPS AMONG PERSONS

EXCHANGE REGULATED BY EQUIVALENCES AMONG GOODS AND SERVICES

PEASANT EXCHANGE

"FACULTATIVE" EXCHANGE BY FOOD PRODUCERS FOR DURABLE GOODS, LUXURIES, AND THE LIKE

REDISTRIBUTIVE PEASANT EXCHANGE

EXCHANGE REGULATED BY A CENTRAL SOCIAL AGENCY; FACULTATIVE

EXCHANGE NOT REGULATED BY A CENTRAL SOCIAL AGENCY

BARTER EXCHANGE

SEVERAL DIFFERENT AND INCOMMENSURABLE STANDARDS OF VALUE IN EXCHANGE

MARKET EXCHANGE

ALL GOODS AND SERVICES COMMENSURABLE FOR EXCHANGE PURPOSES

BARTER PEASANT EXCHANGE

SEVERAL DIFFERENT AND INCOMMENSURABLE STANDARDS OF VALUE IN EXCHANGE

MARKET PEASANT EXCHANGE

ALL GOODS AND SERVICES COMMENSURABLE FOR EXCHANGE PURPOSES

m|h 9/59

Figure 2

Moslem world, a large part of Latin America, and most of southern Asia and the Asiatic island world. One interesting characteristic of some of these peasant economies is the presence of two different kinds of markets in the system, making what has been called a "dual economy."[22] The dual, or better, the plural economy, links the food producer, who retains a subsistence base, with a local native market and also with a world market system. There is a three-way exchange among these elements, which is represented respectively in the village, the native market town, and the "foreign" city.

Redistributive-peasant economies have been present since the beginnings of civilization. Some form of this symbiotic relationship characterized ancient Egypt and Mesopotamia and feudal Europe. It still occurs in the Communist countries, where compulsory deliveries of produce are exacted from a still partially self-supporting peasantry. In China this form of organization seems to be undergoing a radical transformation. The commune appears to be an attempt to expand vastly the consumer-producer unit from family size to local collectivities of several thousands of people, producing mostly for their own needs but also linked redistributively to the national economy.

Peasant economies already foreshadow the commercial symbiosis characterized by the combination of market and redistribution. Some areas of Western Europe and North America are without peasantry, and are entirely organized by these joint principles, with the market dominant. In the Communist countries of Eastern Europe and the Soviet Union, the peasant economy has been preserved or restored within a commercial system dominated by redistribution.

The market not only dominates entirely in some large areas, but penetrates almost everywhere into regions where important commodities for world trade can be produced. There is, therefore, a kind of market fringe around the edges of areas where other economic forms prevail, as along the Guinea Coast of Africa, the Guianas, the lowlands of Indo-China, the oil-producing countries of the Persian Gulf area, and so on. Not only does the market system appear in these areas, it also co-exists through international trade with the redistributive systems of the Communist countries. (See Figure 3.)

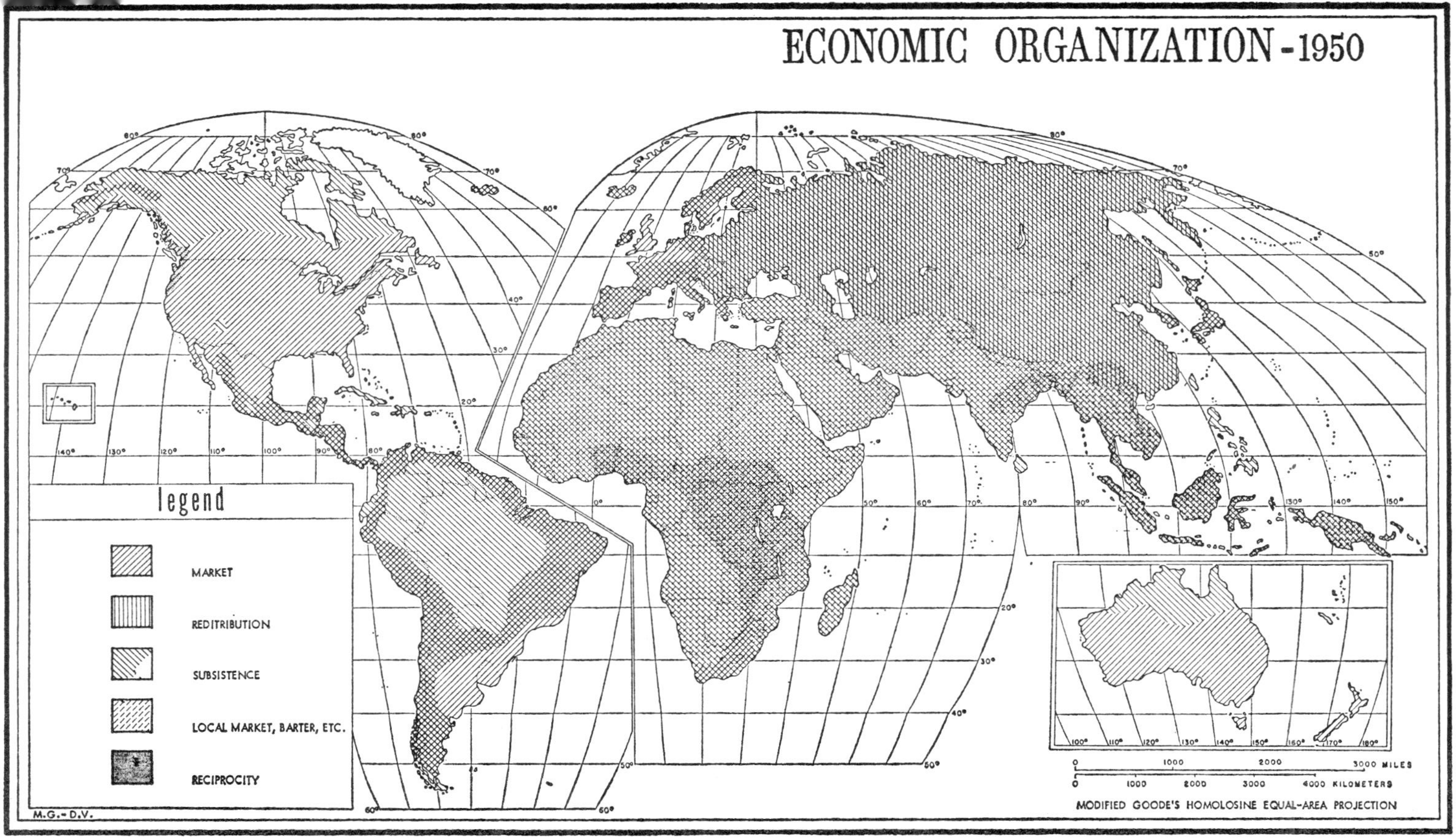
ECONOMIC ORGANIZATION - 1950
legend
MARKET
REDITRIBUTION
SUBSISTENCE
LOCAL MARKET, BARTER, ETC.
RECIPROCITY
0 1000 2000 3000 MILES
0 1000 2000 3000 4000 KILOMETERS
MODIFIED GOODE'S HOMOLOSINE EQUAL-AREA PROJECTION
M.G.-D.V.

Figure 3

GEOGRAPHY OF LIVELIHOOD

WHAT ARE SOMETIMES CALLED the economic *activities* of mankind form a rather different figure on the map than do the systems of economic *organization* discussed in Chapter 5, though the two are related. The so-called economic *activities* will be treated in Chapters 8 and 9. They are the substantive methods of getting a livelihood, and include such things as gathering of wild products and hunting game, intensive fishing and hunting, the cultivation of plants, the herding of animals, and manufacture and services. These activities used to be thought of as appearing in a series of historical "stages" of cultural development, exemplified in Morgan's famous classification as savagery, barbarism, and civilization, and echoed by many later writers. Eduard Hahn overthrew the orderly scheme of development by stages, but many classifications of the types of economic activity are still current. Thurnwald, for example, recognizes nine major types according to social and technical criteria, and V. Gordon Childe refers to three main "stages" of food-gathering, food-production, and civilization, which creates a "surplus".[23] On purely technological grounds, the basic division is between *food gathering* of all kinds, no matter how skillful and productive, and *food production* through the use of domestic plants and animals. There is no such neat division between industrial manufacturing techniques as there is among goods-getting techniques, though the range in productivity between the most ancient stone-working and the work of a modern factory is much greater than that between ancient and modern food-getting. Childe's adoption of "civilization" as an additional economic type, of course, reflects the importance of societal and economic criteria such as the specialization of productive roles and the prevalence of commerce.

The more consistently technological classifications of "economies" in the sense of productive systems, such as those of Sapper and Forde, observe distinctions among tools and techniques used in cultivation.[24] Since there is much difference of opinion as to the number and kinds of cultivation types that should be recognized, authorities differ in the way they draw the map of economic activities. Usually plow cultivation is set apart from cultivation with the hoe; perhaps digging stick and even planting stick cultivation are further distinguished; various kinds of gathering and collecting or harvesting are differentiated, and so on. Any single comprehensive classification of economic activities or livelihood types, depending as it does on even more complex criteria than the classification of formal economies, is hard to justify against its competitors. In the ensuing chapters, however, some of the distributional aspects of relevant technical features will become clear.

We have considered ways of dealing with the problems created by the unevenness of resource endowments. The subsistence and exchange systems and the various symbiotic forms to which they give rise have important geographic implications and their distributions affect other matters to be considered. Let us now turn to a more detailed examination of the material means by which livelihood is produced.

THE MEANS OF PRODUCTION

ARTIFICIAL features introduced by man into his habitats modify the impact of nature on him. They are both the products of his past intervention in nature, and the means of his future influence in nature. The ecological relations of the human individual are vastly modified by the effect of artificial agencies. The technical order is the middle term; it carries man's impulse, greatly modified and magnified, into nature and transmits natural influences to man in controlled and altered forms.

Work and the means of work are under the influence of both nature and man. The human working relation, established through the use of certain artifacts and managed by economies, is not only decisive in man's ecology, it is also a biologically peculiar characteristic of humans.

THE MEANING OF WORK

EFFORT expended in the indirect satisfaction of wants is *work*. It is under social regulation and directly contributes to the maintenance of the artificial environment. As a contribution to artificial habitats, human work is not unlike the activity of some other animals. The different operations carried on by the various kinds of individuals in an ant nest or a beehive, the building of nests by birds, the collection and storage of seeds by rodents, the construction of dams by beavers and of burrows by many rodents and insectivores, are effort directed toward the creation of particular artificial habitat conditions, and must also be counted as work because they make for indirect satisfaction of wants. These other animals, however, engage in work only in connection with the construction and maintenance of their dwellings or with the accumulation of food reserves.[1] In contrast to the work of other animals, human work creates the means of further production, and employs artificially created conditions and devices.

The artificial environment of man is altogether distinctive because it is made up largely of productive goods, or capital, produced by human work and used in the production of other goods and services. Man has been described as a "tool-using animal," but as is well known, many other higher mammals can employ natural objects spontaneously as tools. Tool *making*, however, is peculiar to man.[2] From the ecological standpoint, the possession of man-made production capital is perhaps the chief distinction of human societies, though of course it rests in turn upon the human capacity for culture, speech, and so on. Geographically, the differentiation of the earth's surface is under the joint influences of natural processes and artificial processes induced by man using capital equipment. The so-called "cultural" features of an area—artificial features introduced under the influence of culture—are often just as prominent, or more prominent, than the natural features in whose origin man has played no part. Consider the urban landscape with its square miles of pavement; its towering buildings; its vehicular traffic; its sewers, watermains, and wires; even its air is full of gases artificially generated, and may have to be cleansed by artificial means.

Man, acting directly and alone, registers little effect in nature. A really "wild" human being, with no artificial equipment, would no doubt leave as little visible evidence of his presence in the country as does any other large mammal. What we see of man's effect is to be attributed to the extension of his powers through artifacts, and especially capital or productive artifacts. Capital, furthermore, extends, transforms, and gives specific effect to the movements of the human body, which are otherwise hardly registered.

Work is activity contributing to the creation and maintenance of the artificial environment of a society. This activity is an expenditure of energy. In physics, work refers to the product of a force and the distance its object moves in the direction in which it acts. We shall think of work as movement accomplished by the expenditure of energy.

Work is a physiologic function of the human body, specifically of the contractile muscle cells. It depends on biochemical and biophysical processes that transform energy from one form to another and requires a supply of energy materials to the body for life processes. The contribution of the body in work is movement; the body at work is a mechanism, a kind of motor.

Work in production, then, is movement, carried on by the body and influencing the movement of other things. Nature moves; man's movements are components and guiders of natural movements.[3] The power to intervene in natural movement so as to control its magnitude and direction is what we call *skill*.

Human work can be regarded as applied skills. *Skills* are the expression of cultural concepts transmitted by symbols. They enable man to manage a great complexity of physical movements that result in the utilization of resources, that is, in making natural materials useful to man, or in adding to them the utility of place, time, and form to prepare them for consumption. In another sense, work is the use of resources which are unmodified or already partly utilized.

Finally, work must be seen as the performance of a function in society. The working role of an individual is somehow co-ordinated with the roles of others; it is specialized and forms a part of a larger sequence of activity directed toward specific ends. It takes place under conditions set by the culture and permitted by the society. Human work, in other words, necessarily has economic implications. It is influenced and regulated by decisions taken under a particular form of economic organization. The economic conditions of work concern not only the co-ordination of numerous individuals, but also the spatial arrangement of the capital through which they operate and the natural resources which they exploit. The work of any individual in a given place at a certain time has a specific position and specific spatial associations in the economic organization of his society. Role and place are co-ordinate.[4]

Ten attributes of human work have been listed here, and it will be convenient to construct a more comprehensive definition of them: Work is the performance of social roles at specific times and places. It consists of the expenditure of human energy to perform skilled movements that control the movements of objects in order to add human utility to resources.[5]

This definition encompasses work as physical activity, and does not refer to mental work. Mental activity is an important human characteristic, and should not be overlooked in a discussion of the role of man on earth, but its great importance lies in the very fact that it is not limited by physical circumstances. The freedom and power of man in nature flow from unconstrained thought. We are here considering the limitations imposed on human action by its environments, and cannot disregard the role of thought as it acts through culture in circumscribing action. Even acknowledging that thought affects material action, however, and that environment may affect thought, we cannot assert the opposite idea that environment prescribes thought.

The net effect of work in nature is to control the movement of things. T. Kotarbiński points out that any work accomplished in the external world presupposes "a doer, a sufficient impulse, a material, a product or result, a tool or organ, some manner of acting, some purpose, some deed. . . ." He shows that work is performed through either organs or tools that transmit an impulse or pressure to an object, with or without magnification of its intensity, and for either immediate or delayed effect.[6]

Working techniques are founded on cultural conceptions of the interaction of a human body, as a mechanical agent, with the rest of nature. Work is a strategy of interference in the processes of nature to bring about desired changes. Control of nature depends on understanding nature.[7]

The technical processes are actually simply natural processes of a special kind, for which man only sets the stage. Human action does not usually effect major transformations in natural substances by itself. It depends upon the *natural* interactions of substances and forms to produce desired results. Only in the case of the internal processes of the human body, which are almost all unconscious and autonomous, are significant transformations produced in natural materials by the human organism itself. Insight into the processes of nature, the skillful manipulation of the appropriate environmental conditions, and the massive rearrangement of substances in space enable man to bring about production. This insight, planning and control are functions of abstraction. Man's material role, concerned with movement, is a function of his physical activity.

FACILITIES AND TOOLS

TOOLS, in the widest sense, are movable material objects especially designed for the application of energy in precise and controlled ways for particular mechanical tasks. Usually their respective functions are few and specialized, and their design specific for a given task. The effect of tools is to specialize the human organism for a particular purpose by equipping it with supplementary working parts that increase the effect of its own energy or of energy available to it.

The mechanical properties of tools are often far different from those of the body parts. Energy to operate them is derived from many sources in addition to the human metabolic process.

The use of tools employs refined muscular motions of the human body to bring objects and materials into contact and to produce mechanical effects therefrom. It thus involves also a system of bodily movements which is among the most characteristic kinds of behavioral traits distinguishing the human species.

By the refinement of motions toward greater precision, the increase of uniform and repetitive motion, the augmentation of momentary concentration of energy, the development of more intricate synchronization and programming, and the employment of larger selections of materials, man, with his tools, can increase incalculably his influence in nature. The uses of tools are all in some way systems of movements. Sometimes they involve large components of motive energy from human muscular power; at other times, only the slightest and most infrequent bodily movements are needed to control sensitive mechanisms that employ large amounts of inanimate energy. Without man, however, all the tools and machines of the world would soon be at rest.

The artifactual method of work has the advantage that as knowledge of the world increases, new artifacts may be created which will enable man to apply new techniques, new sources of energy, and new materials to productive tasks. If the productive capabilities of men were restricted to tasks that the body could perform alone, the increase of abstract knowledge would be of little utility. Tools make knowledge work. They help to widen man's experimentations and explorations. As symbols in themselves, tools and other artifacts also help to record and transmit accumulated cultural experience.

The human trait of using tools directs the attention and activity of their users from simple feeding and toward new interest in the seeking out of materials for tools, in their fabrication, and in their use for the making of still other tools. As understanding and technical efficiency increase, men discover and incorporate into habit new ways of exploitation of the habitat. While the effects exerted by animals on their habitat are mainly related to their feeding and shelter, man, with his interest in many materials in addition to foodstuffs, and with his greatly enhanced mechanical powers provided by the use of tools, exerts a much greater influence on habitat. Man can make use of a larger and more varied part of the total content of the habitat than can most animals because of his versatility, adaptability and mobility, and especially his use of tools. Moreover, by extensive transformation of the habitat itself, man produces new conditions for his livelihood. Aided by his tools, man is able to subject the concrete and physical world to the dominion of the human imagination.

Man uses tools to provide consumption goods and services, and capital or producers' goods. *Capital* includes tools themselves, but it also includes other kinds of material objects that are equally important but different in function—we shall call these *facilities*—and combinations of both tools and facilities. *Tools,* as we have seen, are movable objects used to transmit motion; *facilities* are stationary artificial objects whose function is to contain or restrain motion.[8] Most of the capital employed in production in more advanced societies incorporates the features of both tools and facilities, but the technical equipment and installations of the simpler societies tend to be divisible into one or the other category. Facilities are geographically more prominent than tools, comprising such things as buildings, fences, canals and roads, and such compound artifacts as vehicles and vessels.

Yet another kind of artifact merits consideration here: the *symbol,* a consciously selected or deliberately created device to record or suggest an idea or cultural category. All artifacts are, in a sense, symbols; but we have to make a place for those important material creations of man, such as books, flags and works of art, that have no other function than the symbolic, and which still play a vital role in action. As we shall see, the features of the symbol are incorporated in compound artifacts along with those of tools and facilities.

The tool operates as an extension of man's own body, and transmits the motions of the body; the facility is correspondingly an extension of natural objects or a modification of them, and manages natural motion; the symbol is a projection of the mind upon an object. These three are the material means by which man contrives to influence the course of natural events and make them serve his wants, the artificial element in nature that makes man ecologically unique.

VARIETIES OF CAPITAL

THERE ARE MANY possible ways of classifying the technical equipment and installations that are associated with man. Artifacts are often classified according to the particular cultures with which they are known to occur, into ethnographic inventories of material culture and archaeological "assemblages." Such classifications take account of the assumed use of objects, the materials from which they are made, their particular design, the frequency of their occurrence, and their distribution in space and time.[9] A related classification arranges artifacts in order of their historical appearance.[10]

Some scholars have classified artifacts according to their physical characteristics. Thus, in addition to historical typologies of such things as projectile points and pottery in archaeology, and the historical and distributional records of the occurrence of agricultural tools, textiles, house-types, and many other such things, there are typological studies of clockworks, printing presses, textile machinery, steam engines, vehicles, and a host of other mechanical artifacts, and studies also of the chemical industries, dyeing, metallurgy, and so on.[11]

For our purposes, the classification of artifacts according to mechanical and other technical properties is most relevant. Since, however, there is apparently no accepted terminology both general and consistent enough to serve here, we shall attempt to devise one.[12] Our typology will apply terms in common use, restricting their definitions according to certain explicit criteria. Though such a classification of artificial objects as that shown in Figure 4 cannot be sufficient or final, it may at least stimulate discussion and lead to some eventual agreement upon categories and terms.

The first problem is in the definition of the term *capital* itself. As commonly used, the word may refer either to physical objects, that is artifacts, or to the control thereof as manifested in the possession of financial power symbolized by money. Money itself is an artifact in our society, but the symbolic representation of control over other things is its only function; even money in the form of currency is unnecessary to symbolize this control, since it is often expressed simply in written form. We shall use *capital* here in the purely material sense of artificial objects made by man.

The case of money exemplifies the symbolic uses that may be made of material capital. Currency, whether of metal or paper, sea-shells, pelts, stone disks, or gold nuggets, is usually of very little practical utility except as money—that is, as a counter, a standard of value, a medium of exchange, a means of accumulating wealth, and so on. The symbolic functions of currency, in other words, tend vastly to outweigh any other uses it may have; though there are some exceptions, as where wheat or cattle serve both as money and as commodities, as they did in Roman days.

There are numerous other kinds of artifacts whose function is largely or entirely symbolic. In modern Western societies, symbolic objects play a very important part in the dissemination of the cultural pattern and in the conduct of the society's everyday business; moreover, they simultaneously embody some high creative achievements. Everything written or printed is a symbolic artifact—newspapers, books, letters, posters, accounts, and the like. Photographs and paintings and sculptures, and sometimes even buildings also possess symbolic qualities. The peoples of New Guinea and Melanesia have their symbolic ritual headdresses and masks; the ladies of New York or Los Angeles have the same. Insignia, flags, badges, boundary marks, street signs, are all primarily symbols, and so are statues and monuments.

Symbolic functions inhere in many kinds of artifacts in association with other uses, just as many of the actions performed by any individual convey a symbolic meaning to his fellows in addition to accomplishing some task. If these symbolic aspects of man's creations receive little attention in these pages, it is not because their importance is denied, but rather because they are best understood in another context than that of the discussion of the material conditions of human life.

The artifacts employed mainly for their physical effects can be considered according to the ways in which they transmit or restrain motion, the ways in which they transform energy, and the ways in which they incorporate symbolic functions. Employing these criteria, we derive a classification like that given in Figure 4.

Mechanical artifacts are employed either to transmit the motions of the human body, or to restrict the motion of objects. The first class of artifacts is *tools,* the second *facilities.* Tools which transmit bodily motion directly are here called *implements,* and those which transmit it indirectly are labeled *missiles.* Implements are simple and direct extensions of human organs, chiefly of the hands and arms. They transmit motion in the same sense and at the same intensities as those of the connected bodily movements. A pole used to knock fruit off a tree is simply an extension of the arm; it moves as the arm moves. A knife provides the hand with a sharp and firm cutting edge, and produces its effect directly in response to the pressure and draw exerted on it. A hammer, by its concentration of weight, adds force to a blow by the arm, and presents a hard surface against the object struck. A blowpipe channels the force of rapid exhalation into a small space and allows it to propel a missile in the direction in which it is aimed. Missiles, like blowpipe pellets, javelins, and boomerangs, exert the force of the thrower on objects at a distance. Boomerangs and other throwing sticks, incidentally, deviate from a straight course, and might be said to operate like parts of machines in conjunction with the air through which they pass.

Facilities are *containers,* like baskets and pottery, vessels, boxes, buildings, tubes, simple watercraft, and such; *bases,* like floors, roads, and platforms; and *barriers,* like fences, dams, and walls. Some things, like ditches, may belong to several of these categories at once. Facilities represent a rearrangement of features of the environment, or the addition of features to the environment; they control or prevent the movement of solid, liquid, or gaseous material and animate beings. Containers such as houses and clothing serve to protect humans from the greater risks and discomforts of nature. Containers are of great strategic importance to men because they make possible the storage, preservation, and transport of foods and other substances, and because they allow man to "capture" and manage in a restricted space such natural processes as fermentation, cookery, dyeing, and pickling.

Somewhere typologically between tools and facilities lie *cords,* including their use as *knots,* which both transmit and restrict motion. The knot consists of parts moving against one another and partially restricting one another in response to a bodily impulse or natural movement. There are no completely rigid parts in a knot, but in other respects it foreshadows the "machine" which combines the transmission of motion with its restriction.

A *machine* is an arrangement of one or more moving parts in a rigid frame. The inventory of technical equipment of most primitive people contains a large variety of implements, containers, cords, and knots, but usually shows few true machines. Along with their basketry, skin clothing, hammers, adzes, knives, axes, and other tools, their nets and snares, their needles and thread, their clubs and spears, even the simpler peoples may possess a few machines. These may include the mill made up of mortar and pestle, the bow and arrow, the fire-drill, and so forth. Tools in general function as parts of mechanical systems, since they are brought to bear against rigid objects by the body; but since the system encountered here is only partly artificial, it cannot be called a true machine.

A machine consists of a combination of an implement or several implements, which transmit the motion of the body, with a rigid facility which restricts that motion; it both transmits and translates motion. Machines exert their pressure in a direction different from that given by the operator; that is, through a translation. They are often capable of magnifying or reducing the muscular impulses they receive. The simple lever illustrates this property. The wheel is an example of a machine which turns linear into rotary motion. The scissors employ leverage to reverse the motion applied to them. We are all familiar with a great number of different machines operating upon these principles and with other more complicated ones incorporating clockworks and other devices to produce delayed motion.

Most kinds of machines in modern industrial countries are

TAXONOMY OF CAPITAL

EXAMPLES

I. Symbolic .... *Writing, art*

II. Material
- A. TOOLS
  1. Implements .... *Knife, hammer*
  2. Missiles .... *Javelin, boomerang*
- B. FACILITIES
  1. Containers .... *Pot, house, boat*
  2. Bases .... *Floor, road*
  3. Barriers .... *Fence, dam*
  4. Lines .... *Cord, knot*
- AB. MACHINES (simple) .... *Firedrill, bow, cart*
- C. ENERGY CONVERTERS
  1. Prime movers
     a. Engines .... *Steam-engine, internal combustion engine*
     b. Motors .... *Electric motor*
  2. Batteries .... *Storage battery*
  3. Dynamos .... *Dynamo*
  4. Heaters .... *Electric furnace*
  5. Reactors .... *Reactor*
  6. Friction devices .... *Match, percussion cap, etc.*
- ABC. POWER MACHINES .... *Lathe, gun*
- D. INSTRUMENTS
  1. Natural objects .... *Foot, stick*
  2. Tools (=A) .... *Calipers*
  3. Facilities (=B) .... *Basket*
  4. Machines (=AB) .... *Scale, violin*
  5. Power machines (=ABC) .... *Electron microscope, etc.*
- ABCD. AUTOMATA
  1. Manufacturing automata .... *Pipeline, chemical batch plant*
  2. Automatic signals .... *Aircraft warning devices, weather signals*
  3. Calculators .... *Univac*
- *BC. NON-MECHANICAL POWER DEVICES .... *Sailboat, plow, etc.*

* If considered within a comprehensive natural system, of course, all devices using energy are subject to mechanical description.

Not all possible combinations of subtypes are given here. Only the chief and commonest categories are listed.

Figure 4

not operated simply by human muscular energy, but employ
other sources of power, though the operator's bodily motion is
required to control the function of the machine. What we shall
call *power-machines* are examples of this more complex kind
of artifact which combines not only the features of tools and of
facilities, but also utilizes energy from sources other than human or animal metabolism. These complex machines are operated by *prime movers* which convert energy from various
natural sources into mechanical power. The chief categories of
prime movers are *engines,* which convert thermal into mechanical energy; *motors,* which change electrical to mechanical
energy; and other devices such as windmills and waterwheels
for harnessing inanimate mechanical energy. Such facilities as
sails, which apply wind-power to the propulsion of vessels, and
the numerous devices that harness animal power for traction
and other uses, are similar to prime movers except that they are
not necessarily connected with machines, serving instead to
propel implements. Animal power also is widely used to operate machinery for grinding grain, drawing water from wells,
and so on.

Alongside the prime movers is a large class of related artifacts that convert energy in various other ways. We can call
these simply *energy-converters.* Such things as dynamos, just
the reverse of motors, which turn mechanical into electrical
energy; accumulators or batteries, which transform energy back
and forth between electrical and chemical forms; heaters; nuclear reactors; percussion caps; matches; and so forth are included in the energy-converter category.

The great bulk of industrial machines in Western countries
today is composed of power machines and their refinements.
Since ample descriptions of these artifacts are available, we
shall not pause to discuss them further here. It is clear, of
course, that the prime movers, operating in conjunction with
machines, provide a means for vastly increasing the mechanical
power of man and so for expanding his effect in nature. The
energy latent in mineral fuels, and potential in descending water,
wind, and other natural sources, is at the service of man. When
energy is converted to electrical form, it can be transported

over considerable distances and distributed in units of any magnitude, to be reconverted into mechanical form as needed. The development of electric power from various sources, and the adoption of machines designed to operate using it, have made industrial production possible on a much larger and more flexible scale.

The advance in power signified by the progression from tool and container through machine to power machine has been impressive and has played a great part in human progress;[13] but once large-scale inanimate power comes upon the scene, it is the advance in design and use of "instruments" that contributes most to wealth and growth. The case of nautical instruments like the mariner's compass and the astrolabe is a famous instance; men formerly dared not sail far without knowing where the wind was driving them, and the discovery of America had to await Columbus, who knew these instruments but had neither more seaworthy vessels nor more favorable winds at his disposal than others had had for centuries. Inanimate power alone does nothing for man; controlled inanimate power is his slave. Instruments provide the means of controlling this power.

An *instrument* is a specific kind of artifact which transmits energy impulses to the human senses. The essential function of an instrument is not to furnish mechanical energy, though it may do so incidentally; it is to register, through some variation in its own state or activity, the variation of some other phenomenon. The simplest instrument is an object like a stick, a hand, a pace, used to measure linear distance; a stone to measure weight; a basket or a cup to measure volume. Even unmodified natural objects may serve as measures. Simple machines and power machines as well may be specialized as instruments for this function. An old-fashioned balance-scale is a good example of a mechanical instrument, and if we recognize the important role of instruments generally in transmitting symbols, we may cite musical instruments in this same category, and vindicate common linguistic usage. Power instruments include many signaling and communications devices like telephones, radios, traffic lights, vibraharps, electron microscopes, and radar.

Instruments are important in informing man of conditions in the world around him, including those deliberately created by other humans for their symbolic value. They also play an essential role in keeping watch over the use of materials and energy in man's own artifacts: the graduated measuring cup and the oven-thermometer in the kitchen, the automobile speedometer and the tire-gauge, the pressure gauge on the steam boiler, are familiar cases of instruments incorporated into or used with working devices. The function of such instruments is to inform the human user of a tool, container, or machine of the conditions of its operation, and to allow him to manage that operation according to its "feedback."

The operator of a power machine sets it in motion or halts its motion, guides the direction and intensity of its function and the supply of material to it, and otherwise directs its operation through another kind of specialized devices, which consist of small, manually operated machines. Switches and regulators are such devices which are grouped under the term *controls,* and which belong to any kind of powered equipment.

Some kinds of valves, switches, and the like are not manually operated but, once set, they will operate automatically like instruments. These are the simplest kind of *automatic controls.* Powered mechanisms that respond to combined instruments and controls built into them, without the constant intervention of a human operator, are automatic machines. or *automata.* They incorporate automatic controls and associated instruments, and the role of their human operators is reduced to switching the apparatus on and off and to setting the controls to follow some schedule of operation. The machine "observes itself" and does the rest. These automata function either for productive mechanical tasks or as instruments. The so-called machine tools, which can follow detailed instructions and produce other artifacts, are instances of the first kind. We might cite as well all sorts of complicated devices working on a flowing raw material —like oil pipelines, with their tank systems; refining plants, acting as integrated units; and the complex automatic chemical plants and electrical power systems now in use. These are *manu-*

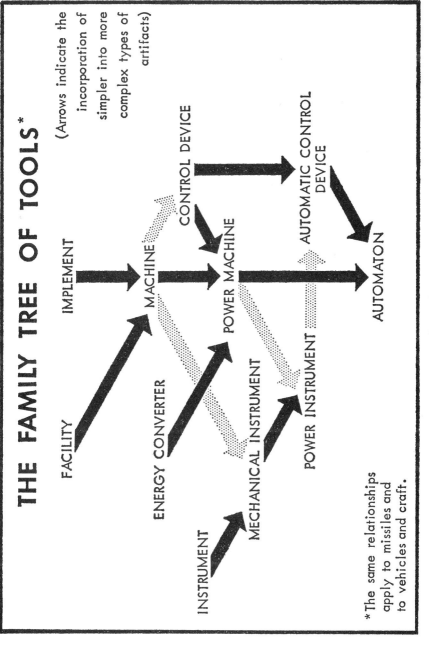

THE FAMILY TREE OF TOOLS*

(Arrows indicate the incorporation of simpler into more complex types of artifacts)

FACILITY

IMPLEMENT

MACHINE

CONTROL DEVICE

AUTOMATIC CONTROL DEVICE

ENERGY CONVERTER

POWER MACHINE

MECHANICAL INSTRUMENT

POWER INSTRUMENT

AUTOMATIC INSTRUMENT

AUTOMATON

INSTRUMENT

*The same relationships apply to missiles and to vehicles and craft.

Figure 5

facturing automata. The second type of automaton, an *instrument*, keeps track of some phenomenon and signals the appearance of given conditions. Radar and automatic air-raid warnings are examples. A related kind of automaton instrument works on symbols, and signals through the use of other symbols. The automatic calculator is such a device. These various kinds of automata can be combined in many ways to form large integrated systems operating under the control of a small number of men whose role is reduced to planning, initiating, directing, and terminating the operations of the system through a master control, and to "feeding" it the power and substances necessary to its continued operation.

Machines, power machines, and automatic machines can be housed in stationary facilities, such as in factories, power-plants, and workshops; or they may be mounted and incorporated into mobile facilities. There are *vehicles* and *craft* without any mechanical parts; others operate with machines, power machines, and fully automatic controls. Vehicles move over land, craft through air or water. The simplest vehicles are the travois, drawn by an animal or human, and the sledge; and the least complex craft are boats made of single hollow logs, sewn planks, skins, or reeds. At the bottom of the complexity scale are skis, snowshoes, skates, inflated skins, floating logs, and lately, innertubes.

The simpler vehicles and watercraft may be carried down a gravitational gradient on land or with a drift in water; they may be pushed, pulled, poled, paddled, or rowed by men; blown by wind, or drawn by animals. Such simple machines as wheels, oars, and tillers are incorporated into vehicles and craft. Self-propelled vehicles, watercraft and aircraft, like the automobile, motorcycle, motorship, and airplane incorporate their own prime movers as well as mechanical driving equipment. Since some railroad trains are operated in conjunction with elaborate switching and signal systems, emergency safety devices, automatic firing, and so on, they function nearly automatically at times, and ships may travel under automatic setting for long periods at sea. Aircraft often are guided by the automatic mechanical pilot while the human operator watches; and fully automatic missiles already can travel great distances, even outside the earth's gravitational field.

DOMESTIC PLANT AND ANIMAL CAPITAL

THE KINDS of capital listed in the preceding section are overwhelmingly mechanical devices. Man is a most peculiar organism in that he augments his bodily powers by the use of artificial mechanical devices. The mechanical influence of man in nature is thus out of all proportion to that of other organisms, and man can employ this influence to improve his ecological lot. The modification of environment toward conditions favorable for human life can go a long way with appropriate use of capital, but some of the conditions most immediately and vitally bearing upon human life cannot be changed by direct mechanical means, no matter how powerful. Man's nature is such that his food supply must come from organic matter, which he cannot yet produce mechanically.

Some human groups use mechanical power to provide artificial habitats for other living organisms upon which their own food supply depends and from which they often satisfy other wants as well. Men select the plants and animals that will inhabit these artificial environments, and so there develop certain domestic species especially equipped to live in them and which become, indeed, dependent on them. Thus, domestic plants and animals are linked to man in an obligate symbiosis.

Domestic plants are responsive to and dependent upon humanly induced artificial conditions for their growth; they are also under the influence of other conditions imposed by the natural environment, which man can modify only little if at all. The nature of the soil and the climatic march of the seasons affect all plants, and restrict any domestic species to certain parts of the earth. Man can extend the range of a domestic plant, partly through artificially disseminating it to all places where he encounters appropriate natural conditions for its growth and partly through trying artificially to modify natural conditions to favor its growth. Crop plants tend to prosper in areas in which the climate is roughly like that of their original homelands; as we might expect, we find that mid-latitude plants have spread across Eurasia into temperate latitudes elsewhere, and that since the Age of Discovery a great exchange of lowland tropical plants back and forth between Middle and South America, South Asia and the Asiatic isles, and intertropical Africa has occurred. Except for a few major crops like the potato and maize, both of which moved out of tropical highlands into higher latitudes, tropical and temperate crops are still distinct. Lesser differences of climate also decree a graduation of crop zones exemplified in the spatial relations between wheat, barley and rye outside the tropics, or by the locations of fruit-growing districts.[14]

Plants adapted to artificial environments vary according to the time at which man uses them, from weeds, vigorous but unwelcome companions of man which are seldom harvested, through crops whose fruit is harvested at the end of a full life cycle or season, to plants which are harvested before this final stage of development. Since the cultivation of a crop may take place under conditions suitable for only a part of its life cycle, its geographic distribution may be extended accordingly or the expenditure of effort in creating an artificial environment for it may be reduced appropriately. The growing of grains and clovers for hay under cool climates in places where they cannot produce seed is an example of this; the seed for each year's sowing must be imported. Many ornamental plants are grown far outside the range of their normal climatic toleration, and never come to fruit or even to flower; consider the non-fruiting banana plants and date-palms used decoratively in California gardens. A crop like cotton, which can grow as a perennial, is treated in most places as an annual, and the maintenance of its artificial environment ceases after the picking of the bolls, so outside the tropics, the plant usually dies after the harvest.

The growing of crops requires two kinds of intervention by man: he must provide and maintain an appropriate environment for plant growth, and care for the plant itself. The life of the plant is customarily thought of as comprising the stages of germination, establishment, vegetative growth, flowering, fruiting, and seed dispersal.[15] At each of these stages, the condition of the natural environment may be different; the requirements of the plant vary from one stage to another as well. The role of the cultivator is to adjust, insofar as possible, the changing states of the environment to the changing stages of plant development, and to guide the development of the plant in the particular direction he desires.

The environmental conditions affecting germination are such as: space in which the seed may sprout; a proper moisture content in the immediate surrounding air layer and soil; a particular intensity and periodicity of sunlight; appropriate ranges and periodicities of temperature in soil, air, and water; suitable chemical conditions in the soil and water (and also perhaps in the air); protection from parasites such as bacteria, fungi, and animals; and suitable mechanical conditions for support, orientation, compression, or other needs of the seed. To each of these requirements may correspond an appropriate measure on the part of the cultivator.

Most important during the germination stage is the correct choice of season and site for planting. The site must, furthermore, be cleared of previous cover, not only to permit germination but to prepare for succeeding stages of the cycle. Moisture may be provided artificially through irrigation; the soil may be conditioned by tilling to receive the seed and to prepare for subsequent growth. Man may also need to repress the growth of insects, to scare off birds, to poison rodent pests, or to control the development of bacteria and fungi by treating seed or soil in advance. He may prepare the soil for the later nutritional needs of the plant by fertilization before planting.

During the establishment period, the structure and texture of the soil are especially important, for the rootlets of the new plant must come into contact with a proper supply of air, water, and nutrients. The plant may now require particular conditions of shade and mechanical support, and the cultivator may have to suppress competition by weeding out adventitious plants.

In the vegetative stage, the plant has new requirements that must be met. Cultivation, irrigation, pest control, weeding, and fertilization may take place again in this period of growth, but certain measures in the care of the plant itself, like trimming, training, and thinning, may be added.

In the flowering stage, the plant presents still more requirements. Of course, often new weather conditions appear too. The cultivator may repeat what he has been doing, or may devote his effort to the protection of the inflorescences of his plants, or to the promotion of their pollination by insects or other agents. At fruiting, similar needs for protection may impose themselves. In both the flowering and the fruiting stage the cultivator may interfere by thinning out the plants, removing some of the inflorescences, or knocking off young fruit to improve the quality of his crop.

The harvest can take place during any stage from vegetative growth onward, depending on the purpose of the cultivator. The harvest is the most urgent of all his activities because spoilage occurs rapidly. Grains dry and shatter, fruit turns mealy, root crops rot in the moist soil. Furthermore, since the seasons are changing, bad weather may threaten the crop directly, or make the use of mechanical harvesting equipment difficult.

A multitude of different ways exist to condition environments to meet the needs of growing plants, and some of them will be considered further below. A word is necessary, however, about the other kind of work in which the cultivator engages— the care of the plant. Some measures in plant care have been mentioned already. The most fundamental is the selection of material for planting.

There are two kinds of planting material: seeds and clones.[16] In certain species, a piece of vegetative material may simply be planted in the soil, carrying unchanged the genetic composition of the parent plant from which it was taken, and will form a new individual. Plants which reproduce vegetatively as clones are of course less variable than seed-reproduced plants, in which mutations appear that can be transmitted by selection. Among clone plants are potatoes, bananas, and manioc (cassava); there are a great many more such crops, mostly in the tropics. Seeds, unlike clones, can be selected for breeding to develop given genetic characters, and over several generations of genetic variation the crop can often be changed quite radically. Both clone and seed material must be preserved, guarded from pests, and kept from spoiling between harvest and planting. Clone material can often simply be left in the ground during this period.

Clone reproduction from the planting of shoots is mostly peculiar to the American and South Asian tropics; but another type of vegetative reproduction, including grafting, budding, and similar techniques, perhaps originated somewhere in the middle of Eurasia and has spread widely. These techniques are usually practiced in connection with orchard crops and ornamentals.

The care of plants, especially horticultural care, often involves the trimming off of some of the vegetative body to conserve the strength of the plant, to beautify it, or to remove diseased tissue. Man also trains plants to grow in certain shapes or on supports like the espalier, pole, and trellis. Flowers or fruit are often thinned to improve the crop or to protect the branches from too heavy a load. Wounds on a woody plant may be attended with care by the grower. There are thus a number of operations that can be performed on the plant itself, and the kind of cultivation that emphasizes this care is commonly known as horticulture. It is most widely practiced in the cultivation of ornamentals and orchard crops, and in tropical root-garden cultivation.

Transplanting also needs mention. This again is primarily a horticultural technique, but it is used also for the world's most important food crop, rice, which is grown in fields rather than in gardens. Transplanting usually means the preparation of two quite different sorts of artificial environments for the plant at different stages in its cycle: a seedbed and a field. The seed is allowed to germinate and then the young plants are set out in the field.

Domestic animals are in a situation which resembles that of plants in that they too are fitted especially for and are dependent upon an artificial environment provided by man. Most domestic animals are less sensitive to climatic difference than are plants, and man can disperse them more readily and widely. They are more able to fend for themselves, and most of them, except in times of extremely harsh weather, need simply the provision of food. The most important characteristic of a domestic animal, in contrast to a wild one, is probably its ability to tolerate the approach of, and even the touch of, man.[17] To be classed as domestic, an animal must exhibit this characteristic in all situations; most essentially, it must breed freely in captivity. On this score, the otherwise tractable elephant is excluded formally from the roster of domesticates in good standing.

Feeding, of course, is not the only service which man performs in caring for his domestic animal symbiotes. He protects them from great heat and cold by putting them in facilities such as stables, kennels, coops, cotes, and hutches; he provides them with drinking water, defends them against predators, doctors them through illness, grooms and bathes them. In some remote places, human females suckle the young of dog and pig. It is also not irrelevant that humans provide genuine and needed companionship for some domestic animals, and vice versa. Finally, man exercises a selective control over the breeding of his stock, thereby influencing the development of new strains. The dull and domestic sheep is quite unlike his crafty and agile ancestors in the hills.

CROPLAND AND CULTIVATION

Cultivation is man's intervention in nature to promote the growth of domestic plants. Since this intervention closely reflects the capabilities of artifacts and natural energy at man's disposal, we shall consider the techniques of cultivation and the use of land under the respective categories of capital named above.

The form of cultivation that is no doubt most ancient, simplest, and least productive is that in which implements alone are used. The implements include the axe, the knife, a digging or planting stick, and other elementary devices. No animal energy is used in this kind of farming, though small domesticated animals may be kept. The preparation of plots for cultivation is accomplished through the cutting and burning of existing vegetation; this also helps to control pests and may enrich the soil in mineral nutrients. The crops grown under this system are not unique to it but are found in other kinds of cultivation.[18] In the tropics, upland rice, maize, manioc, yams, taro, various kinds of beans, squashes, and sweet potato are prominent among them; other crops, including small grains and pulses, are grown in the few places where this system still appears in the higher latitudes.

When implements alone are used, crops are often grown mixed. More care is devoted to the individual plant than to the "field," which may remain full of stumps and logs; but even so, not much care is given to the plant. A frequent change of planting sites is commonly practiced, and it is therefore sometimes called "shifting cultivation." Because of its method of establishing clearings it is also known as "slash and burn," and several local names for it, like *milpa, tavy, chitimene* and *ray,* have been introduced into the literature.[19]

The name "horticulture" may best be applied to a second form of cultivation, one in which both tools and facilities are used. Under horticulture the artifacts are designed with great ingenuity, and much is invested in their installation. The hoe is the characteristic tool, but there are many other specialized implements. The land is almost always permanently cleared, and the surface is carefully remade to retard runoff and to accumulate organic fertilizers. Elaborate networks of canals or ditches may be constructed to provide irrigation water for the crops.

The cultivator still gives the individual plant rather than the field the most attention. A horticultural site is more a garden or an orchard than a field. It often contains a variety of plant species, and much hand care with special tools is given to the growing plants. In the Andean highlands, potatoes, quinoa, ulluco, oca, and other peculiar vegetables are grown by this method. In Middle America in pre-Conquest times, cacao was grown thus; and around Mexico City, the famous *chinampas* were floating gardens devoted to horticulture in the form of intensive hand cultivation of vegetable crops. Horticultural crops of the Far East include the mulberry, a host of vegetables like beans, radishes, cabbages, peas, taro, ginger and many other spice plants, and numerous fruit trees. Horticultural farmers in Melanesia and New Guinea grow yams, taro, breadfruit, coconut, pandanus, tacca, and other plants. The crop plants of Indonesia and South Asia resemble those of these areas. In Africa, bananas, yams, pulses, many kinds of millets or large-seeded tropical grasses, and several peculiar root crops are grown horticulturally. The horticulture of the Mediterranean area is characterized by the presence of the fig, olive, vine; walnuts, almonds, chestnuts, and pistaccios; many kinds of fruits; and, in the south and east, by the date.

One of the marked peculiarities of both horticultural and slash-and-burn systems is their lack of domestic draft animals. Animal traction is practically not used in this kind of cultivation, and of course is not well suited to work with individual plants. The plow and other animal-drawn implements are associated with fields, not gardens. This does not mean that no domestic animals are kept in places where these methods of cultivation are practiced, however. The pig, for instance, is very common in the Asiatic and Pacific horticultural areas, and sheep and goats are kept in the horticultural complexes of the Mediterranean area. In New World "milpa" regions, turkeys were commonly kept.

Agriculture, here, is that form of cultivation in which tools, facilities, and machines are used together, and work animals are usually present. The plow in its various forms, the waterwheel, the wheeled cart or barrow, the scythe and flail are typical machines and implements of agriculture in this sense, and they are commonly associated with draft animals like oxen, horses, and buffaloes. Agriculturists permanently clear the land; they may also terrace, bank, ditch, or otherwise modify it to control the flow of water and to conserve soil components. They frequently use irrigation, and sometimes construct irrigation facilities which are very elaborate and costly to build and maintain. The farmer uses the rotation of crops or fallowing as well as or instead of heavy fertilizing to maintain the fertility of the fields.

His attention is chiefly directed toward the care of the field rather than to the care of individual plants. He usually plants the crop seed by broadcasting or drilling, rather than by inserting clone stocks as in horticulture.

Agriculture thus defined is practiced in two essentially different ways: one Oriental, the other Occidental. Farmers using the Oriental practice concentrate upon rice-growing and use many of the techniques of horticulture, such as: the elaborate development of terraces, irrigation systems, diked fields, and other facilities; the transplantation of seedlings; the intercropping of several kinds of plants; the hand care of the crop; the heavy use of organic fertilization; and the permanent use of fields without rotation or fallowing. Practice within the system of Occidental agriculture, which includes farming in Europe and in areas settled by Europeans, as well as southwestern Asia as far as northern India, northern Africa, and perhaps even northern China, involves the plowing of dry fields, usually unterraced; the broadcasting of seed; the cultivating of usually only a single crop in each field; and the rotating of crops and fallow fields. Western agriculture exists side by side with various local horticultural traditions; Eastern agriculture has become fused with a horticultural system.

The crops of agriculture proper are small grains (including rice, wheat, barley, rye, oats, sorghum, millets, and now maize), many pulses, still mostly localized (like the broadbean and pea in Europe, the lentil and chickpea around the Mediterranean, the pigeon-pea and others in India, the soybean in the Far East), and corresponding local varieties of rootcrops (like radish, carrot, turnip, and beet), along with the members of the cabbage family, the melons and cucumbers, and tree fruits and berries.

A newer sort of cultivation is *power agriculture*. This is a form in which men employ power-driven machines—of which the tractor is the most typical and widespread. The power of machines replaces the toil of animals. There are not only power machines cultivating, but others especially for constructing facilities. Irrigation and drainage systems are characterized by the use of power pumps and other such devices. Artificial fertilizers are commonly used. Almost all of the operations of cultivation are performed by machines driven by motors or engines. The fields are like those of Western plow agriculture, and the crops the same, except that there is an increasing concentration on "industrial" crops like sugar beet, cotton, and oilseeds. Animals are raised for meat, milk, hides, and wool; and mechanical devices driven by inanimate power are often used in their care.

Automatic power machines are just beginning to be used in cultivation. They are employed on a limited scale in hydroponic systems to control the physical and chemical properties of a solution substituted for the soil. Automatic devices are also used to control atmospheres in greenhouses and laboratories. In these forms of cultivation there is neither garden nor field, but a tank or soil-bed. The plant is tended individually, at present, but perhaps this is only because this form of cultivation is still largely experimental and a luxury specialty. The crops grown are chosen for experimental purposes or for a high-priced market. Automatic cultivation is found in hundreds of laboratories and experimental greenhouses, in some military bases and pioneering stations in high latitudes, and in commercial hothouses that grow vegetables and flowers for market under glass.

A word should be added about animal husbandry. The use of animals for traction is standard under agriculture proper. Where power agriculture has arisen, parallel developments have taken place in animal care, and modern dairy men, for example, in a highly industrialized country, tend to equip their farms with power-driven machines of many kinds. Except in true agriculture, however, the raising of animals is not closely integrated with cultivation. Large herds of animals were kept until very recent times by separate social, and even national, groups peripheral to the agricultural populations—wandering as pastoral nomads in lands unsuited to cultivation. The nomad always had some relationship with the agriculturist. Indeed, a great many pastoral groups were part-time farmers. The raising of animals remains a specialty in certain types of country under power agriculture, and the growing of crops in places becomes subservient to it.

CAPITAL AND NATURE

IF WE RANK technical equipment and installations on a scale from simple implements through facilities, machines and power machines to automata, we may expect a commensurate increase at each step in the power of man in nature. The more advanced his technical means, the more a single individual can do to his surroundings; the wider his effect can extend itself in space; the deeper into the earth, and the higher into the heavens his power will reach. The powers of society also grow, in fact at a rate greater than the individual's; individuals working together in a systematic way produce a greatly magnified effect. Of this subject we shall have more to say in Chapters 8 and 9.

When humans possess implements only, they can hardly scratch the surface of the ground. If they are cultivators, however, they may actually modify their surroundings to favor food production. People having only implements are pitted little more than evenly against the beasts of the wild. Missiles are as important to them as are implements in the hunt; they avoid dangerous close contact with large predators, and can only reach more timid and less wary prey. Fire is their greatest ally, but they can scarcely control it. Having no facilities or machines, such folk cannot even produce very efficient tools, since they can only utilize materials which are already at hand, easily worked, and which already possess the appropriate physical qualities for tools. Men can do little clearing of the forests with rude stone axes, even when they are abetted by wild-running fires. Generally, where men still have only simple equipment, the forest still stands. Wild game can be driven with fire but probably cannot be exterminated with simple weapons, unless it is already on the wane through other causes. The exploitation of mineral materials is confined to carrying off what can be picked up from the surface or scraped out from shallow depth. Stones suitable for projectile points and the like, salt, pigments, and bright pebbles and shells are available.

When facilities are constructed men can store foodstuffs. They can accumulate large amounts of seeds, roots and other products, and seeds may sprout or some shoots may grow from these accumulations in the vicinity of dwellings or refuse heaps. Men drive game into prepared snares, corrals, and pits, sometimes using fire. They may line springs, enlarge pools and may build or dig aqueducts. Living sites are constructed having house platforms, palisades, squares and streets, refuse heaps, and so on, though these facilities remain fairly primitive in many cases. An even larger variety of facilities comes to be associated with cultivation.

Mine shafts can be sunk into the earth, and the subsurface is opened to exploitation. Certain peoples who do not practice cultivation but who can build facilities at this technical level produce many ingenious fishing and hunting devices. The folk who build elaborate facilities, whether cultivators or not, are capable of serious depletion of game and fish supplies; of intensive modification of living sites and their immediate surroundings; and of some use of subsoil minerals. They can sometimes effect great changes in native vegetations.

Peoples with machines are capable of proportionately greater effects, and correspondingly larger benefits therefrom. Not only the direct impact of their machines, but their widened needs for materials and their improved means of communication play a telling part in changing the environment. Some hunting peoples, as well as cultivators, use machines, and they have been very effective predators, able to feed themselves in a specialized way from selected herds of ungulates or from particular sea mammals. It was machine-using folk, too, who cleared the great woodlands of middle latitudes, which could not be breached with simple implements. As long as the power to drive machines must be furnished by animals or humans, however, the machine proper has probably not been an instrument of wholesale destruction of vegetation or mineral deposits. Machines used in cultivation do expose poorly protected soils to washing and gullying, and they do allow men greatly to modify the soil surface. The use of machines in hunting also greatly increases man's predatory pressure on animal life.

The capabilities conferred on man by power machines are prominently registered in nature. There is such a large literature of alarm on this topic that detailed comment is superfluous here. Man can dig miles deep into the earth, plunge to the depths of the sea, soar far into the heavens and aspire to reach the moon. With power machines men can chop mountains to pieces for ore, move hills, force rivers to run backwards, crack the atomic nucleus with a flash and a mushroom cloud, and attempt to create living matter in the laboratory. Nature is at the mercy of man, and man acts blindly at his own peril. Great risks and great rewards await him.

The role of the automaton is still to be revealed. It may act mightily for destruction, sucking up insatiably the wealth of nature, or it may make possible a calculated adjustment to the natural conditions impinging on man's life and work, which will reduce the hazard and the folly of uncontrolled exploitation of nature. Automatic calculators are already being used to inform mankind of the prudent course, and the automatic machines may someday manufacture goods (and services) in ways so much more efficient, economical, and sparing of natural resources that man's stewardship of earth may greatly improve as his power grows. The issue probably depends more upon the ways in which societies and economies are organized than upon material technique itself.

Although the consequences of man's technical activity for the conditions of his life in nature are the subject of our discussion, only a sketch of the impact of techniques upon environment has been possible here. We need to know how capital is fitted into man's environment and managed by his societies before we can tell more of its effects. We shall begin a consideration, then, of how the artificial environment is spatially structured by different peoples.

CHAPTER SEVEN

ARTIFICIAL
ENVIRONMENTS

THE TERRITORY occupied by any human group is distinctive
not only for the particular disposition of plains, hills and valleys,
streams and lakes or coasts, forests, grasslands, deserts or
swamps it exhibits, but also for the particular arrangement and
character of the works of man within it. The homeland of every
society of men has its own characteristic dwellings, workshops,
granaries, ceremonial places, monuments, lines of communication and routes of travel. Usually it has its own peculiar aggregation of domestic plants and animals, and its own sorts of
vehicles, tools, watercraft, machines, and so on. Artifactual
features appear in many forms in the landscape; there may be
canals and dams, mines and quarries, fields and gardens; isolated farmsteads, hamlets, villages and cities; and, linking these
together, trails and waterways and highways, signals, wires and
conduits.

THE VARIETIES OF SITES AND ROUTES

THE ARRANGEMENT of artificial features of a territory reflects both the nature of the land and the work of man. Considered abstractly, this arrangement is a spatial pattern for human action, a maze of sites of activity and routes of movement. Its component features are distinguished according to the particular natural features with which they are associated, the particular kinds of artifacts present in them, the particular individuals or groups frequenting and using them, the particular times at which they are occupied and used, and the particular linkages among them. They are differentiated functionally into several distinct types of installations.

At no two places are the arrangements of sites and routes exactly identical, but their component elements are distinctive to each society and occur repeatedly in particular associations. The activity of each human group, with its own cultural and social constitution and a given sort of territory, tends regularly to produce a characteristic association of features in space.

Human work, necessarily a social phenomenon, depends upon mutual support and the transmission of artifacts and skills from one individual to another, and results in the creation of a common artificial habitat. The essentially social character of work, together with man's comparatively large body size and peculiar feeding habits, make it virtually impossible for any human group, of whatever size, to subsist permanently and exclusively on the natural products of any single place. As a mobile animal man depends upon his locomotion for survival. As a social animal in addition he derives his livelihood from the combined activity of all the members of a social group, and shares in the joint use of a common territory, of a size appropriate to satisfy the combined wants of all the group.

Human work is directed toward the utilization of natural resources, that is toward making ready and suitable for human consumption the potentially useful materials found in nature. Since the productions of nature change with the seasons and resources are usually distributed widely and irregularly in space, one of the chief objects of work is to make materials available at times and places other than those at which they occur naturally, that is to add *time utility* and *place utility* to objects. The means of creating these utilities are storage and transportation. The other main object of work is to create "form utility" through modification of the composition or form of objects.

The technical proficiency of a society in transporting, storing, and modifying goods, which rests upon its command of appropriate capital and skills, is one of the major controls of the spatial order of an artificial environment. Other controls are the natural character of the land, with which we cannot deal in detail here, the internal relationships among members of the society, and necessary principles of order governing the operation of the technical system.

The relations of human beings to their artificial environments have been described as falling into two classes, which we called production and consumption. Among the installations and equipment produced by human work, some part serves primarily consumption and the rest functions as means of production. The spatial arrangement of artificial features, and their function in the livelihood of man, can best be understood if we observe a distinction between the installations devoted to production and those serving consumption. To be sure, both functions may be found in a single installation, and production, especially, is carried through continuously in many successive sites, but the location and significance of production and consumption sites and routes, respectively, respond to quite distinct influences.

Both sites and routes may be called "installations" of man. Usually, as we shall discover, they are made up of what have been earlier referred to as facilities. In the case of production they almost always contain very specific kinds of equipment as well—tools and machines performing particular functions. The category of productive installations, furthermore, should include both sites of human activity such as manufacturing, and sites provided for the growth and life of domestic plants and animals.

Let us think of *production* as the sum of the numerous processes concerned with transferring natural materials from the places where they occur to places of use, and with altering and combining them in place or on the move to make them into usable objects and materials. At least two different classes of locations are already implied here: the places of occurrence of the materials with which production starts, or *natural resource sites*, and the places of their ultimate use. If, as is usually the case, the two respective locations are not identical, there is some route between them which the materials follow in the course of production; let us call this a *route of circulation*. If the material taken from the resource site is to be transformed in some way, this too will take place at some definite spot, in which particular capital equipment for the operation is assembled; the site of transformation we shall designate as a *manufacturing plant*.

Production may take the form here suggested, running from a resource site along circulation routes and through manufacturing plants until its product reaches the consumer, or it may be carried on in one spot where, in artificial habitat conditions provided by man, plants and animals are grown for human use. After a time, the product from the growing site is again moved along circulation routes and sometimes through manufacturing plants to its consumers. To the several classes of productive sites must therefore be added *cultivated lands*.

The preceding classes of locations have all been those concerned in the production of goods, that is of material substances and objects. Production also may include the provision of services by one individual to another, and we may distinguish a corresponding class of productive sites as *service centers*.

Five classes of productive installations have been named: natural resource sites, circulation routes, manufacturing plants, cultivated lands, and service centers. In addition to their functions in production, these sites and routes are also places of consumption, for they are created and used by human beings who provide suitable living and working conditions for themselves, and in them certain materials and equipment are committed or consumed in production. One further kind of installation is that primarily devoted to consumption as such, namely the habitual places in which dwell the consumers themselves.

We shall refer to that portion of the artificial environment where human beings actually live as *settlements*. Not only dwellings, but also the working places included in settlements, are especially conditioned for human living, and so there is very considerable overlap between the category of settlements and the several categories of productive installations.

Though it is easy thus to distinguish conceptually among a number of kinds of artificial environmental features, the degree of their functional differentiation varies among actual human societies. The number of such distinct kinds of sites and routes, and the variety of specializations within each, indeed may serve as excellent indices to technical advance. The extent of a society's ability to control its environment may be indicated by the relative abundance and complexity of the means it possesses to do so, as well as simply by the amount of transformation it effects in its physical surroundings. The degree to which a people is independent of the circumstances and cycles of nature around it is fairly well expressed in the differentiation of those kinds of sites and routes, like manufacturing plants and service centers, that reflect in their localization the influence of technical and social specialization more than natural situation.

The simplest folk, of which the Semang of the mountainous interior of Malaya are a good example, have only routes of systematic wandering among the sites of natural production that they use; even their dwellings are temporary, and there is no such thing among the least modified of them as a cultivated field, a specialized manufacturing plant, a particular place where services are offered.[1] Their techniques are simple, their life precarious, their numbers small—it all hangs together—and they leave hardly more than a faint footprint, a whisper, and a fading shadow in the Malay mountain forests where they move.

If anything expresses plainly "man's relation to environment," it is the way man uses and invests environments. The environment he uses is, or soon becomes, an artificial one; the way he occupies it and makes use of it is sensitively registered in forms that man creates. The composition of an artificial environment, and the relative location of its several features, are clues to and controls of man's ecology. These features themselves respond to what may be called "ecological" conditions; their character and location tell much about man, and become more comprehensible when studied as the issue of an interplay between two sorts of influences. These forces are, first, the constant adjustments and coordinations among the individual members of the whole complex of man-made installations (their "synecology"); and second, the relationships between an installation and those outside elements of its own surroundings that affect it (its "autecology").[2] Without insisting on this ecological terminology, we may apply this way of thinking to problems of the character and location of the features of the artificial environment.

We should not expect to find a Buddhist temple in a Bantu *kraal*, a steel mill in a camp of Eskimo, a field of pineapples in Saskatchewan, or a decayed log full of pale white grubs providing a feast to a crowd of Chicagoland suburbanites. In each of these unlikely cases, we might ask, "How can this be here?"

This is a most useful question. It leads, once the location of certain features is known, to consideration of what are the necessary conditions for their presence. Whether it be a grove of *Sequoia Sempervirens* that demands summer moisture and high winter temperatures and so grows only near the northern California coast, or a filling-station that depends on heavy automotive traffic and therefore occupies a corner of a busy intersection, the location of any geographic feature conforms to certain "rules." The very presence of a redwood tree or of a gasoline pump presupposes certain circumstances in the present or the past that have allowed it to become established, and certain impulses or processes that have been sufficient actually to accomplish its establishment. In other words, both necessary and sufficient conditions exist for its occurrence. The occurrence of a ghost-town suggests that the conditions for its establishment no longer obtain. On the other hand, those conditions identified as necessary to the incidence of a certain feature do not automatically ensure its appearance. For example, although the climatic and soil conditions of the Congo Basin are well suited to the establishment of Amazonian or Indonesian forest trees, such trees do not occur there: the impulse to their diffusion is lacking. But by the same token, the recognition that the necessary natural conditions for the growth of the Brazilian rubber tree (*Hevea*) were present in Malaya has led to the creation there of a major rubber-producing center.

When necessary environmental circumstances are known, the establishment of crop plants becomes possible in new areas; and, indeed, once the requirements of any artificial feature of environment are known, its development can proceed wherever the appropriate conditions are found. To dig a mine, a body of ore must be present; the geologic structure must be such as to support the excavation; facilities must be available to ventilate, drain, and shore up the interior passageways; means must be at hand to dislodge the ore, to carry it, to pass it on for processing and use. This is only the *autecology* of the mine; it is also necessary that the ore be of some use to a society, that other installations exist to smelt and form it, to transport it, and to sell the final product, and that it have a potential body of consumers. Given all these and other necessary conditions, the mine still will not be sunk until someone takes the initiative to acquire jurisdiction over the land and rights of exploitation, to assemble a crew of workmen, to install the necessary equipment, and to arrange for disposal of the product of the mine; this initiative is the sufficient condition for the presence of a mine. We cannot tell where or when it will obtain, but only where it might be possible and where it may not. By asking "How can this be here?" of the various and specialized kinds of artificial features, we equip ourselves to estimate the potential development of particular territories under various cultural and societal forms.

Similar questions can be asked about a bridge—where can it span the stream? what routes shall it link? by what technique can it be built? what material may be used for its construction? —and about a cornfield, a watch-factory, a beauty-parlor, or an apartment house. In each case, regardless of great differences among the circumstances that influence its location, the *ecology* of any feature involves first both the natural conditions of the place and the characteristics of the people concerned; and, second, it involves the composition and layout of the existing artificial environment. All of these circumstances are effective only as they bear on a particular feature at a given spot.

Let us now systematically consider some of the principles governing the location of the artificial features of man's environments —resource sites, routes of circulation, manufacturing plants, cultivated lands, service centers, and settlements.[3]

NATURAL RESOURCE SITES

RESOURCE SITES are the artificial features most strongly influenced by natural conditions, namely by the amounts and availability of useful materials at given places. Their exploitation is governed further by the cultural evaluation of materials, by the technical means at hand, by the organization of the economy using them, by the volume and rhythm of production in the society, and by the employments made of the resource.[4]

What is a resource to one human group may be of no conceivable use to another. The Navaho wandered for a long time over deposits of uranium without finding a use for those ponderous rocks, and only when the warlike powers discovered deadly uses for the mineral did the deposits become important resources that have made the tribe rich in recent years. Obsidian and flint, however, which at one time were important resources to native peoples on this continent, have almost ceased to interest anyone. The amount of the resource that is used may differ, too, according to the culture. The Indians anciently extracted modest amounts of native metallic copper from the seams of the Upper Great Lakes region, but could not have dreamed of the vast exploitation since undertaken by the Whites in the copper country. On the shores of California bays, however, there is evidence, in the form of shellmounds, that certain local shellfish were much more heavily used in prehistoric times than at present.

A *natural resource* is something that can be used and that occurs in nature. Three primary factors in the location of a resource site are, therefore, a human group that knows how to utilize the respective material, a suitable concentration of it in nature, and means of access for the people concerned to the place of occurrence of the material. A natural resource site is always located where some particular natural conditions occur: at a given mineral deposit, stand of trees, habitat of animals, source of water, display of scenery, or other natural supply of the desired commodity. It is always located within territory occupied by or open to a society that can make use of it, either for its own consumption or for trade. It is always located on a route that links it with the eventual consumers of its product.

Any artificial feature is a part of a larger system. Consequently, a second set of factors influencing the location of resource sites, and for that matter of any class of installations, is the specific spatial arrangement of the artificial complex, and its character, capacities, and connections. The usefulness of a substance does not depend simply upon knowledge of its potentialities and a desire to have it. It must be possible for the resource finally to appear, transformed, in some product or products which are desired and used. For these, there must be outlets from producers to consumers—either supermarkets or peddlers, country fairs or auctions, government "handouts" or allotments, i.e., exchange—or a household subsistence unit. Facilities must be available to transport and to store the product as needed on the way. There has to be some way of making the raw material into finished goods, and this means a chain of different manufacturing plants, each of which itself requires all sorts of preconditions. There must be suitable processes of manufacture, implying not only technical knowledge, but also suitable tools or machines, skilled workers, accessory materials; and if the product is assembled out of many different components, each of these in its turn represents a potential limiting factor, a bottleneck, in the production of the final article and therefore in the scale of use of the material from a given resource site. The amount of copper mined will eventually react to the amount of tin available (at suitable prices) for combining with it in brass and other alloys; to the demand, in turn, for brass as a material for making fittings, gears, and such; to the capacities of existing plants for smelting and refining copper, making alloys, machining the metal, and assembling final products; to facilities for distributing to users the products in which the metal has been employed; and of course to the volume of use of the product, which is under the influence of a host of other factors connected with the structure and economic management of the whole artificial complex operated by the society.

The separate individual influences of all these factors cannot easily be assessed as they impinge upon a given resource site. Their joint effect is represented, however, in the price that the given commodity brings or in the quota assigned by a production plan under the more complex forms of socio-economic organization. In the less complex societies, technical limitations on production restrict the exploitation of a given resource. To take copper again as an example, when we know the geological conditions under which the ores occur, and the locations of the various copper deposits, it may be possible to tell what mines in the United States and Mexico will be in operation and even what their volume of daily production may be if we know current prices for the metal and the costs of operation. In the Soviet Union, the current production plan may indicate the rate of production. Technically, much more copper could be produced in either country than is in fact produced, and many more places might become resource sites for the exploitation of copper ores than are regularly in use. In an African society where copper is used mainly for making bracelets, however, the expenditure of time and manual labor in getting out the ore, smelting and refining it, and manufacturing the bracelet severely restricts the scale of exploitation. Nowadays, in some parts of Africa, although copper bracelets and necklaces are still made, copper is no longer mined or smelted—it is easier to get it from stolen telegraph wires.

Technical capabilities and social and economic organization, as they differ from one group to another, clearly have a great deal to do with the kind of places at which the sites of natural resource exploitation are located, and with the scale of their operation. The sufficient impulse that brings into existence a resource site and initiates its operation springs out of human enterprise. When natural environmental conditions and the state

of artificial environment are such as meet the necessary requirements, the exploitation of a new mine or forest or fishery or
stream may be undertaken. Whether or not the exploitation is
in fact undertaken does not depend simply on the presence of
these necessary conditions, however, but upon the active part
of a human individual or group in assembling the necessary
equipment and constructing the necessary facilities, engaging
personnel, gaining control of rights to work the resource, making
provision for the transport and disposition of the product, and
planning the operation. This enterprise need not arise automatically in response to opportunity, nor is its scale dependent
simply on the extent and quality of the resource. Enterprise
displays an "all-or-none" quality; if it occurs at all, it must
create a unit of operation of a proper size to make effective use
of capital equipment, labor supply and raw material, as well
as to meet demand; it must adjust to competition from other
producers; it must bear the costs, perhaps, of providing suitable
living conditions for its workers. It must be able to assemble
means of doing these things at a cost which leads over time
to profitable operation. Therefore, enterprises do not often grow
from infinitesimal beginnings, but spring up abruptly, on already
a more or less large scale. This is just as characteristic of the
technically less advanced societies as of the most advanced
ones. Just as a hydroelectric plant, backed by a great reservoir,
does not grow up gradually and just as there is not a hydroelectric plant of appropriate size on every stream, it can be
observed that Mexican Indians looking for firewood concentrate
their attention on those parts of the woods where branches are
most thickly strewn about, and that a day's hunting trip of
these Indians is not willingly undertaken in regions where the
game is scarce.

The scale and rate of operation of the productive establishment, and the quality and quantity of the natural endowment,
then, restrict the choice of resource sites. The constitution of the
economic unit regulating production also plays a most important role. Enterprise and resource exploitation are small within
kin-based societies and subsistence economies and much larger

under some forms of exchange. If a given territory and its human population formed a stable and isolated unit, with a fixed or slowly changing productive plant, the selection and development of resource sites might be regular and predictable. As it is, there is a constant realignment of different natural endowments with different production complexes. Bolivian tin, Venezuelan oil, Labrador ores, Burmese teak, Icelandic fish are exploited not to serve local demand, which is negligible, but to supply the world. The corresponding resource sites are linked not merely to local productive complexes, but to much more highly developed ones in other parts of the globe. Their location cannot be comprehended without a knowledge of the structure of their economic connections. The relative under-development of resource sites in some places thus reflects among other things the economic forms that govern work. Commercial forest exploitation in Amazonia or Indonesia cannot amount to much at present, despite the wealth of the forests, because of poor exchange mechanisms and poor facilities for transport. The Bushmen do not exploit the salt deposits of the Kalahari for trade, for they scarcely trade; nor did the North American Indians or the native Siberians pay much attention to fur-bearing animals until the French, the Dutch and English, and the Russians and Chinese, began eagerly to trade with them for furs.

We cannot exhaust these matters here; subsequently we shall consider both the technical, social, and economic organization of particular kinds of groups, and their bearing upon the exploitation of natural resources and the location of resource sites. We shall be equipped to deal more adequately with the sites exploited by particular peoples when more about their organization and capabilities is understood.

ROUTES OF CIRCULATION

THE ROUTES along which men, materials, and messages move bind a society together. They make the reticule on which are strung the sites of work and rest; they are the paths along which flow the myriad streams of raw and half-made goods in process of production; they form the links between each local group of humans and the thoughts and presence of its fellows.

There is no human group without well-accustomed routes of movement; none is altogether stationary, and none wanders aimlessly. Numerous places, widely separated, are known and visited even by the simplest folk, and they follow familiar pathways on their rounds. A family of Bushmen knows every track, waterhole and sheltered hollow in the desert. The arid territories of the Seri are crisscrossed by established trails between important sites, which the inhabitants regularly follow. In every neighborhood of every great city, people habitually travel, almost unthinkingly, over private routes selected from the maze of streets.

Circulation routes, be they routes of man's own travel or pathways for his goods and messages, always come from somewhere and go to somewhere. A network of circulation is defined by the points it connects, and their locations guide the selection of the routes. The route's course in traversing the intervening country depends upon the character and volume of the traffic, the technical properties of the route, and the nature of the space across which it leads.

Topography itself has much to do with the layout of communications lines. For most purposes, a trail, an unpaved road, a surfaced highway, or a railroad seeks high, firm, and well-drained ground. It avoids steep grades, and crosses hills and mountain ranges through passes. When a stream is encountered, the crossing may be a shallow ford or a bridge. A fallen log, a rope of vines, a plank, may serve as bridge, or it may be an elaborate and expensive structure carrying heavy mechanical traffic. The change of surface with the seasons, too, must be taken into account. In the wet period many of the cart-roads of the tropics are impassable to any but oxcart traffic. In high latitudes, the winter, when the frozen streams serve as highways for sleighs and when men on skis or snowshoes can move freely, may be the best time for surface travel.

Routes of travel over water also must respect natural circumstances. Small boats and giant ships require sheltered docking places. Craft must follow courses which avoid submerged rocks, erratic tides, stormy days, and icebergs. Their travel is limited by weather. Air travel, too, must observe the weather and the surface conditions for landings and takeoffs, and must heed the presence of high mountains and the approach of violent storms.

The routes on which goods are moved are usually the same as those of men's travel; they also exhibit the same relations to topography and surface properties. Lines of pipe through which commodities are moved are a peculiar case. They are built so as to avoid steep gradients because of the extra pumping cost that would be involved, and are laid out in the straightest line possible to reduce the cost of their operation.

Wires for messages and electric power are affected by special problems—like lightning, the accumulation of hoarfrost, interference by tree branches, disturbance by perching birds, and so on. They tend, on the whole, to follow the routes selected for lines of travel and transport. Some kinds of message apparatus transmit their impulses without wires or other material facilities; however, even radio is disturbed by electronic interference.

The relations between circulation routes and the whole artificial complex are no less influential. The great technical differences among the kinds of circulation found in various parts of the world are expressions of great inequalities of technical and socio-economic integration. The amount of traffic, the kinds of surfaces used, the vehicles and craft employed, their rate of movement, and their frequency of operation all depend on the character of the particular artificial environment; and all these factors are highly important for the development of the routes of circulation. The firmness and width of a road surface bear definite relation to the traffic that it carries; so roads in areas where vehicles are few and light tend to be less developed than where heavy, rapid power vehicles are found in abundance. The state of the roads reflects the complexity, the intensity, the magnitude of movements that are indicators of technical development and economic integration.

The process of exchange of goods and services relies upon

the physical movement of goods and persons; thus the relative development of exchange relations hinges on the development of transport. Furthermore, guarantees of order, mutual trust, and just measure, the standards of agreed value and the very vocabulary of economic intercourse upon which exchange depends are maintained only with the aid of suitable means of communication, control and supervision. Communications lines serve to inform, and to maintain agreement and stability as backgrounds for exchange. Upon exchange, in turn, rests the whole structure of technical and spatial specialization that permits productivity to develop.

In summary, the necessary conditions for development of a route of circulation are the presence of suitable natural conditions and of two or more sites to be connected. The nature of the route will be conditioned by the character of the sites and the traffic they transmit or generate. The output of a mine or forest or fishery, under given conditions of production, demands a route sufficient for a certain volume and weight of traffic. The movement of goods from one manufacturing plant to another requires certain kinds of vehicles and routes.

Personal travel also demands special accommodation, and personal preference affects routes of circulation. Fast, spirited horses and camels which have their own route types have long been bred especially as mounts to be used in war. Sleeping cars notwithstanding, trains are rapidly giving way to airplanes in Western countries, because of their lesser speed. The passenger automobile, wasteful but convenient, is popular everywhere that people can afford it and the roads are at all passable.

Routes and other circulation media are often constructed by public agencies. The cost of creating a circulation network is so great that individual enterprise is seldom able to provide it; and where governments themselves do not undertake construction, they nevertheless tend to underwrite it. It is in the interest of a public agency to improve the bonds that hold the society together so as to increase its productivity and unity. The improvement of routes may be, as we have seen, essential to economic development. It cannot be assumed, however, that better routes of circulation are in themselves sufficient to bring about a dramatic surge toward prosperity. Many costly roads have been built which failed to bring financially proportionate rewards. If the necessary conditions for successful promotion of increased traffic are not present, the road itself can do little. In some parts of southern Mexico and Central America, the chief use of the highway is as a place for the Indians to dry corn and beans in the sun.

It is often possible to choose among several means and routes of travel or shipment, or several ways of transmitting messages. Each line of circulation available may offer particular advantages of speed, low cost, comfort or security. The relative rewards and drawbacks of travel abroad by sea and air are known to many of us. In many countries, it is possible to travel farther and more comfortably in a day on horseback than on foot, but travel by horse is more expensive. In these countries often no roads are suitable for automotive travel, and, in such places, these days one flies if his mission is urgent and he can afford to.

For certain commodities, slow, reliable, low-cost movement is preferred; and much bulk freight moves by water or in slow trains. The oxcart is another slow mode of travel used in many parts of the world for bringing in the harvest over muddy roads, and for carrying goods to places off the beaten track. Many places still exist, in the Orient and the mountainous parts of Central and South America, where most freight, and even passengers, are carried by human porters.

Among the means of sending messages, considerations of speed must be balanced against those of cost. Postal service, telegraph, and telephone are now accessible in most of the world, and are increasingly rapid and costly in that order. Messengers are slower but sometimes surer. The press is an inexpensive communicator of general distribution that is more detailed in its information but less prompt than radio.

In many countries there are several complementary networks of circulation. Thus, on many isolated coasts and islands there is a very restricted installation of land trails and cart roads for short-haul transport, and boats are used for travel or for longer distance shipping. Foot-paths cross and recross the auto roads of Mexico, carrying entirely different traffic, and often rutted cart roads form yet another net. In the United States heavy bulk cargoes move slowly along the coastal waterways and in the canals on barges, while less bulky and more costly freight is transported by railroads and distributed from the railheads by trucks, and the most urgent and expensive shipments go by air. On a country path in the Far East one may see loads being carried on the backs of human beings, slung across the shoulders of other bearers on balanced poles, pushed in barrows, hauled in animal-drawn carts; one sees other things being transported simultaneously by men passing on bicycles, by boats gliding along nearby canals, by trains puffing smoke in the distance, by auto trucks, and by the airplanes snarling overhead.

All of the many kinds of transport and transmission found in a complex society, and all the routes of circulation associated with them, are located according to specific and necessary conditions. They are affected by both the gross physical requirements and the general technical means, and also the most refined and specialized demands of the whole complex of artificial features. The networks of circulation are indispensable to the function of that complex, and are a faithful indicator of its character.

MANUFACTURING PLANTS

MANUFACTURING takes place during certain phases of the movement of materials from natural resource sites toward consumers. Manufacturing plants form nodes upon the continuous paths of production flow, and must, therefore, always be located along the routes of transportation.

Materials move into an artisan's workshop or a great factory, into a rustic cauldron or an automatic refinery, are there transformed, and move out again to other stages. Manufacturing techniques involve the subjection of materials to physical or chemical change under controlled conditions in a restricted space, in a definite order, and on a strict schedule. The substances in process may be combined in stipulated proportions with other materials, as iron ores, coke, limestone and alloy metals are mixed in ferrous metallurgy, and as acids, cellulose and other reagents are blended in making synthetic fibers. Whatever the industry, materials are in movement and are simultaneously being modified.

Manufacturing is the use of one artifact to make others; it is a universal trait of man. Even prehistoric man left his campsites littered with chips knocked off in the fashioning of projectile points and stone knives with rock hammers and bone tools. All societies use various implements and containers in gathering and preparing foodstuffs. Their weapons, basketry, nets, grinding stones or pottery are frequently manufactured through the use of other special artifacts. Specialized equipment for making clothing and for building is also found among most people. Woodworking tools like axes, adzes, and wedges are known from ancient sites and from very simple modern communities. All across northern Eurasia and arctic America, people use needle and thread to sew their tailored clothing, and the needle has been around at least since the Upper Paleolithic era. Personal ornaments of shell used by many peoples are made with special drills, and pigments like ochre used to decorate the living or to sanctify the dead have been ground on special palettes since very ancient times.

Manufacture has perhaps always been associated with human dwelling places. The satisfaction of the so-called "primary needs" for food, clothing, and shelter is ultimately accomplished only at the place of consumption; and at least some of the final stages in the preparation of food, some modification and maintenance of clothing and ornament, some repair and housekeeping around the dwelling, are found in the consumer's residence in any society. Most human households in the world today still grow or gather most of their own food, preserve it in various ways, store it, and cook it as needed. They usually build their own dwellings, and some still produce their own clothing from materials that they provide for themselves. The dwelling is the chief place of manufacture in most societies, and even the American housewife who defreezes, unwraps and oven-warms her television dinner is engaged in a last step in food processing. Furthermore, even where very little home manufacture is practiced, the manufacturing plants of a specialized industrial system are almost always clustered tightly beside the residential quarters of their workers in the towns and cities.

Here, then, are two characteristics of the location of manufacturing plants (including domestic manufactories) in any society: they occur 1) along routes of transport between consumer and resource sites, and 2) in proximity to the dwellings of their workers. The terrain upon which the plant is built must be firm enough, well-drained, and so on. Sites for manufacturing plants are selected, within these restrictions, according to particular needs, the plant being drawn more or less toward resource sites, transportation facilities, consumer outlets, settlements with particular kinds of labor forces, or certain kinds of service centers, as its nature demands.

Plants which process a very large bulk of raw materials of low unit value can often be found in close proximity to resource sites. Thus, one finds cement factories where clay, gravel, and lime crop out in large amounts together; chemical factories around salt brine wells; refineries in oilfields; ancient stone workshops around flint and obsidian exposures; pottery-making villages where good clay is at hand.

Frequently a manufacturing nucleus grows up at the end of a route of low-cost transport connecting it with contributing resource sites. Sawmills are built at the confluence of rivers draining forest country, down which logs are floated to them. Steel mills are often located at deep water ports to which coal, iron ore, and lime can be moved cheaply. Alumina is made at tidewater from bauxite carried in by cheap water haul, and is shipped on to power sites for making aluminum. In many modern industries, a great number of different resource materials are utilized, or a great many component parts and sub-assembly sections are brought together from other places. The technical requirements of the necessary operation influence plant location. In heavy metallurgy, even the supply of water (as a resource in itself) and of proper natural conditions for waste disposal, can be considered factors of location. The American automotive industry, involving much complicated assembly and specialized parts manufacture, is concentrated in one area so that distances between contributing plants are short. The positions of natural resource sites and of contributing plants, which are virtually equivalent in this case, are influential factors in the location of manufacturing plants. Their effect is often expressed through relative costs, or difficulties, of transport.

Since the reason for production is, in the last analysis, consumption, the location of potential consumers plays its part in the process of plant location. In most human societies a preponderant part of all manufacture takes place upon the consumer's immediate premises and involves his own labor. In a similar way, in exchange societies, the concentration of buying power interacts with transport costs to influence the location of manufacturing plants. Location in proximity to the consumer reflects not only the influence of differences in transport costs, but also the effect of local tradition and of the characteristics of the goods concerned. The various peculiar kinds of Japanese footwear, for instance, are produced only in Japan, and certain sorts of pottery are made traditionally in certain Mexican villages for the local market. (The same Japanese make American flags, and the same Mexican Indians fashion clay figurines to sell to tourists, however.) Beer is brewed close to its drinkers or bottle factories to save transport. Bread is baked near its eaters from easily-stored flour.

Labor forces also have a bearing on plant location. In some cases, men with particular skills are available in only a few places. Thus, diamond cutters used to be concentrated in a handful of Dutch cities, and the English names of textile materials testify to the great localization of certain skills in the textile industry in the past. The concentration of skilled persons is related not only to the massing of particular kinds of manufacturing plants in certain places, but also to the provision of distinctive services in these centers. New England used to have a concentration of skilled textile workers, textile-machinery plants, and commercial services associated with the textile industry. The town of Petaluma, California, boasts the "world's only chicken drugstore," providing specialized pharmaceutical service to the numerous poultry ranches in the vicinity.

Labor's demands play their part. Some manufacturing enterprises have moved to Puerto Rico and to the southeastern states to attain savings on labor costs (as well as on taxes). Guild control of skilled workers in the Middle Ages had something to do with the specialization of different towns in various kinds of manufacture.

Commercial banking facilities, technical services, transportation and storage facilities, and so on, are among a host of factors which influence location and must be taken into account. Services such as police, upkeep, maintenance of equipment, finance, and the like, are directly effective; and are indirectly important as they affect living conditions of plant personnel. In some fields of American industry, notably in engineering and machine-building enterprises connected with military projects, special amenities of the plant's surroundings are offered as an incentive in personnel recruitment; and the choice of sites for plants may be guided by this consideration.

The effect of various of these factors upon the selection of sites for manufacturing plants differs, it is clear, from one branch of industry to another, and probably from one country to another. It may be extremely difficult to identify any one decisive influence among these factors in a given case. In the countries where specialized manufacturing in large plants is practiced, the technical conditions are generally similar, but the cultural and social characteristics of the labor force, the financial system, the services and demands of government, and other such influences are varied. Soviet industry, for example, shows a different relation to existing population distribution than does German. Inherited traditions of skill are of less consequence in California than in New England in determining the location of plants employing highly-trained specialists; and amenities undoubtedly play a lesser role in locating engineering plants in Japan than in the United States.

The physical characteristics of sites themselves are, in the case of manufacturing plants, much less decisive for location than are the artificial features connected with the site, and the characteristics of the respective human populations. Manufacturing plants are less responsive to natural influence, and more so to the influence of man and his works, than are resource sites or routes of circulation.

CULTIVATED LANDS

MOST OF MANKIND depends for food on cultivation—man's intervention in nature to promote the growth of domestic plants —and animal husbandry. Cultivation is a complex relation among human beings, their crops and livestock, and the soil, climate, wild vegetation, and so on. The location of the cultivation sites is therefore strongly under the direct influence of natural conditions, especially of soil and climate; of social and cultural conditions among men, and of their technical activities; of the biological character of the crop or herd; and more particularly, of a complex interplay of all these elements.

Cultivated land is land where crops grow or animals feed, by our definition. Thus the crop or herd is the critical element in the question of its placement. A crop plant or a domestic animal is the product of artificial selection by man, a kind of artifact in itself. It has certain ecological requirements, and a geographic range that is set by critical conditions in the environment at particular periods of the organism's development. The range itself of a domestic plant corresponds to an artificial situation in which the domesticated species is exposed to an outdoor climate and a natural soil, but afforded some protection against competing species, provided with moisture and nutrients, and otherwise shielded by man. It represents not the widest possible area in which the plant could be brought to maturity and reproduction by any conceivable means—probably this could now be done anywhere for any plant, given sufficient investment —but the area in which the plant is, or could be, grown profitably at present.

There are large areas where plants simply are not cultivated. In addition to the oceans and other water bodies, most of the territories at latitudes above 60° are excluded because of low temperatures and frozen ground, and large expanses of desert are without sufficient moisture for plant cultivation. In mountainous regions, frequently little surface is level enough and large enough to permit cultivation. Less than ten per cent of the world's land surface is suitable, under present practices, for plant cultivation. The range of animal husbandry, disregarding species differences, is less restricted, and herds graze the Arctic tundra and the sparse grasslands and brush of deserts. Certain biotic limitations, though, like tsetse infestation, produce a restriction of the range of herding. The geographic range of particular species of domestic plants and animals need not concern us further here, however.

Given an ecologically suited crop, a favorable topographic situation, drainage, soil, and microclimate, a natural vegetation amenable to removal, and pests subject to effective control, there remain further necessary conditions for cultivation. The site must be close enough to the dwelling place of its user to allow him to devote adequate time to its care at all the proper periods in the yearly cycle. Moreover, it must be served by such facilities as are necessary to tend the soil and crops. The cultivator must possess the required techniques and equipment to provide the essential habitat conditions, and also to make some use of the crop after harvest.

Cultivated lands are therefore located in some proximity to settlements, permanent or temporary, depending on means of transport available and work requirements. Farmhouses planted among the fields are common in many regions of the world. The peasants in some countries live in compact villages, around which their fields extend for several miles in each direction. If fields suitable for cultivation can be had only at a considerable distance from the village, a temporary camp or village may be established near them while the crop is being tended; this eventually may grow into a permanent settlement. In the United States, where distance is hardly a barrier, some wheat farmers live far away from their fields, and visit them only a few times a year. Some of the Asiatic nomads, like the Kirgiz, formerly sowed fields of grain in the hills, then wandered off with their flocks and did not see the field or crop again till harvest time. It is usual, however, to find that lands in cultivation are closely associated with some human settlement nearby. The reverse is also true: in most areas of the world, the great preponderance of settled habitation is found in, or immediately adjacent to, food-producing land.

It is usual also to find that cultivated land depends closely upon certain facilities. In the Sahara, the growing of crops takes place only in oases, where wells and canals supply them with water; in Turkestan, Iraq and Arizona, the cultivated lands hug the river courses, from which pumps and canals bring water to them. The inhabitants of small isles in Micronesia and Polynesia in former times laboriously built up gardens in pits dug in the coral rock, and the people of Western Ireland and the Scottish Isles used to wrench out enough granite boulders to make a hollow in which peat, kelp and scarce soil could be made to serve as a growing bed for potatoes. In Peru, Java, Luzon, and many other places, large-scale engineering produced terraced hillsides to be used for agriculture.

Fences, too, to protect the crop, and roads and paths, are often found in vital association with cultivation. In Central America, wherever the women raise pigs and chickens to secure cash income, green vegetable crops are doomed unless a tight fence is built; in southern Mexico, one of the common causes of personal violence is the invasion of a man's corn fields by other people's livestock. Fencing is often time-consuming, but crucial. The need for access to the cropland, too, is obvious. Where fertilizers must be brought in, or heavy equipment is used, a road may be necessary. The harvest must also be got out and taken to a storage place. There is a good deal of variation in the need for roads, depending on such factors as whether the cultivator uses a machete and digging stick or a tractor-drawn plow.

Other facilities are required for processing and storing the harvest. Small-grain farmers need means of threshing and winnowing their grain, places to store it away from rats and insects, and perhaps places to mill and to bake. In the more rustic grain-growing regions, one still finds threshing-floors, village granaries, and mills driven by animal- or water-power. In general, for a crop to be grown, thus for lands to be cultivated, a series of facilities of artificial origin must be built to serve—in addition to the production of the crop—its transport, storage, preservation, and even processing for use. There can be no cultivated lands that are not aligned with such facilities through proper connections.

Clearly, the location of cultivated lands responds to many of the same influences as does the situation of natural resource sites. Both depend on certain natural preconditions, on suitable facilities, and on proper outlets and means for using the product. In commercial societies, where crops are produced for sale, other factors come into play, namely, those that weigh in the spatial placement of manufacturing plants. Commercial agriculture, like manufacture, is influenced by the quality of its resources (soil and climate), the nature of its labor supply, the position of its potential consumers, and the existence of auxiliary installations elsewhere in the artificial complex. Many crops which are capable of bringing a high return on the market can be produced only at a few favored spots with a given combination of climate and soil; citrus fruits and cranberries are good examples. The demand for seasonal labor at low wages may further restrict the area in which a crop can be successfully produced for commerce; migrants can be counted on only where there is enough work to reward them for their travel; this may mean that several successive crops must be harvested in the same area. Transport facilities are not equal everywhere. The use of refrigerated railway cars and of fast trucks is feasible only where the concentration of growers using them is sufficient to provide adequate demand for these expensive services. Sorting, preparing, and packaging argricultural products require facilities at high investment; and, again, commercial crops are restricted to regions where such facilities are present.

A large proportion of the Brussels sprouts and artichokes consumed in the United States is produced in a narrow strip of coastal lands from northern Sonoma County to San Luis Obispo in California. The mild winter and the foggy cool summer weather are essential to the crops, and the crops thrive on the black, limey, highly organic soils of the Central Coast. However, artichoke and "sprout" production is not conditioned only by the natural situation. The most economical kinds of farm machinery require level surfaces and light soils; these are widely found on the coastal terraces. The crops require much hand labor; local laborers and migrants are available at planting, weeding, and harvest time. These crops need careful grading and packing; these are accomplished by trained local workers, mostly women, working in the established packing sheds of the area. The financing of Brussels sprouts and artichokes is a delicate affair, requiring good acquaintance with the risks and rewards involved; local bankers, buyers, and brokers are familiar with the conditions affecting loans on crops; and the packers and shippers know how to estimate risk in transit and marketing. Under existing patterns of circulation, the peculiar concentration of favorable climatic, soil, and topographic conditions, of adequate facilities, of skilled growers, brokers, and packers, of transport equipment, and of labor at the right times, gives the Central Coast area command of these agricultural crop specialities despite its great distance from their main markets. Similar situations could be shown for many other commercial crops.

SERVICE CENTERS

THE PRODUCTION of services is associated with distinctive installations and spatial order. Helpful acts of kindness, friendship, or respect are widely practiced throughout any human society, but another kind of services demands special skills and appropriate equipment, and is associated with particular statuses and performed only in certain places which we shall call *service centers*.

Services are performed for people. Since service cannot be transported and stored, the dominating factor in the location of service centers is ease of access for their beneficiaries or consumers. Services are usually provided in close proximity to the habitations of their users. Even many small and backward settlements have temples and shrines where religious devotions can be carried out, craftsmen's installations where tools and other equipment are made or repaired, marketplaces where goods are exchanged and shops where they are sold, a headman's hut, council house or village office in which political and administrative functions center. In a large city, infinitely more and very specialized service agencies are concentrated amid the large settlement they serve.

Two types of services can readily be distinguished. Services to individuals singly are different from services to a society as a whole; each is furnished by different kinds of agencies, and each often displays a different spatial order. *Public services* are performed by individuals and groups selected and maintained by or for the whole society. They are permanent and comprehensive; they help to guarantee the normal conduct of life by all members of society. *Private services* are available to all or to some members of society at their own discretion; and they are not necessarily available everywhere or at all times. Whether a given kind of service is performed by public, private, or intermediate agencies depends on the constitution and circumstances of the society concerned.

Typical public services are religious rites and the care of sacred places; the maintenance of law and order; defense against foreign enemies; the expression of belief and feeling of the group through monuments and festivals. Almost any settled society possesses institutions dedicated to these functions and places set aside for them. Temples, palaces, monuments, and fortifications are usually the most imposing things built by a people. The lavish colonial churches and civic buildings of today's Mexico eclipse entirely the ordinary dwellings of the people, and have parallels in the splendid pre-Cortesian ceremonial and political centers of Oaxaca, the Valley of Mexico, Veracruz, and Yucatan. The great architecture of all times is associated with religion, government, and war.

Other functions and facilities, associated with services such as education, communication, the arts and sciences, the care of the destitute and infirm, and recreation, also serve the needs of the society as a whole; but these are not always fostered by public agencies. In many societies, such provision for education as exists is made by religious agencies concerned with training a priesthood or with initiating young folk into ceremonial life.

Religious concerns, too, have often lain behind artistic achievements and the development of science and invention. The improvement of communications and the exploration of new lands, on the other hand, have proceeded from military activity; and military needs have also made invention welcome. The temple, in the Orient, was formerly often the only school, and the monastery in medieval Europe was the home of erudition and the refuge of the homeless and the sick. The Chinese, Greek, and Roman literature of geographic exploration is written by commanders of the military forces or agents of the state.

The services of the "free professions" are more nearly private in character, and are seldom furnished by public agencies. Such are medical care, the safekeeping and lending of money, private counsel and representation, and entertainment. These services are provided by professions endowed with a certain public dignity and obligation, and particular semi-public places are constructed for them. Hospitals, banks, law-offices, and theaters, or their counterparts exist in many different societies.

The bulk of private services is devoted to the provision and care of material goods. In non-commercial societies these functions are performed by members of the household, but in commercial societies particular agencies in addition devote themselves to carrying, storing, displaying, advertising, and selling goods, and to the repair, cleaning, and preservation of goods. The great mass of service agencies in these societies is made up of warehouses, shops, markets, and of maintenance establishments of all kinds. In the most complex technical systems, the provision of specialized goods and services by such agencies is essential to producers as well as to the consumer. Garages service automotive equipment used in production; skilled maintenance men serve the elaborate machines used in industry; stores supply specialized parts for mechanical assemblies; dealers supply paint, lubricants, solvents and cleansers, and other accessory industrial materials; enterprises sell raw materials, fuel, and power.

In Indian Guatemala, goods are bought and sold in periodic markets to which the people come from all over the highlands. In the villages, there are few retail stores or none. An occasional itinerant peddler makes his rounds, and a few men in the village may be skilled as blacksmiths, barbers, carpenters and the like. In many other societies, too, the trade in goods and the provision of services not available in the household are accomplished through the public market days and by the work of part-time specialists in the community. This is typical for the services in peasant villages. It is the city that represents the full development of services, and that indeed lives in utter dependence on services.

An urban settlement has to contain a service center, for it does not produce sufficient goods of the right kinds to allow each household to feed itself; and it needs exchange, not only to provide for the supply of goods to households, but also to give outlets to the specialized work of its craftsmen and laborers. Service centers, in other words, when their personnel are traders and full-time specialists, must be urban—in the sense of being oriented to exchange and to the presence of sufficient complementary services to assure a livelihood for their personnel. A distinction must be observed between this sort of service center, in which urban conditions are essential, and those characterized by public services and sometimes professional services, but which have no connection with trade and private service. In the latter instance, an elite may live in settlements apart from the villages, which are dedicated to religion, administration, and learning. Such small but important settlements as the sumptuous Maya ceremonial centers, the great tombs and temples of Egypt, and the Cambodian temple complexes, are not cities in the usual sense, yet they were the supreme centers of their respective societies.

The several types of service centers follow quite distinctive patterns in location. Religious, administrative, legislative, judicial, and military services are usually provided by agencies having a definite and limited territorial jurisdiction. In tribal societies, the scope of all the corresponding institutions is coextensive with the population and territory of the tribe. In the European feudal order, religious needs were served by a universal church; but military, legal, administrative (and indeed also private) services were vested in the manor or the town. In

Japan and China, religious life was organized around a family unit with its own shrines, graves, and rituals, and the larger community provided for larger religious functions and other public services. In modern commercial societies, there is a formal territorial division of public service agencies, expressed in the parish and diocese, the ward and township, the municipality and county, the judicial districts, and the military zones and fronts at various levels. Each such territorial division has specific boundaries, and the respective function is usually discharged in a central agency—the cathedral, court, or command post. The institutions serving particular public functions in a given territory ordinarily have exclusive jurisdiction therein, and the whole of a country is divided into a number of complementary territorial units for each public function. The composition of these subdivisions reflects the distribution of population, differences in history and tradition, special problems, and so on. Thus, Congressional districts in the United States are allotted by census population; the Mother Lode counties of California are smaller and less populous than most of those settled later and less hurriedly; and irrigation agencies are concentrated, in the United States, in the drier regions of the West.

The public services ordinarily are organized hierarchically. A province or state is composed of municipalities or cantons; a city, of wards or quarters; a bishopric, of single parishes; an army, of corps and regiments and battalions. A territorial gradation complements the hierarchy of authority.

Professional and semi-public services tend to show an altogether different distribution. These reflect the residential preferences of professionals, the areal distribution of income groups, and the concentration of commercial activity. In Mexico, the proportion of physicians to total population is much higher in the capital than in the other towns and cities or the countryside perhaps because the medical school is situated in the city, and particularly because there are unmatched amenities there. Small town banks are being closed all over the United States as the automobile makes possible an ever-greater concentration of business in the larger and newer centers. Many more professional gardeners work on Long Island and the San Francisco peninsula than in all of rural Texas, because of the much greater demand for their services in fashionable suburban areas.

Professional and semi-public services of all kinds, presumably, tend to cluster together, so that most medical specialists are likely to be where there are also most theaters, exotic food-shops, and foreign bookstores. The clientele of professional specialists makes use of many different kinds of special services, and the presence of other pleasant services attracts the professionals themselves to certain places. It can be noted, finally, that this class of services exhibits much less hierarchical organization than does the public service class. Private agencies are seldom assigned an exact delineation of territorial jurisdiction, or a clear graduation of authority.

Private services are furnished by commercial enterprises spread wherever there are concentrations of consumers. Maintenance services tend to be related to the presence of certain kinds of necessary equipment, and are in fact an instance of a very strongly consumer-oriented branch of manufacturing. In a society where handicraft holds sway, it is practically impossible to differentiate between these services and manufacture. What a tinker, cobbler, tailor or blacksmith does in such societies falls into an intermediate category. In commercial societies, special maintenance services are always directed to nearby consumers, and are dependent upon a supply of materials and equipment. Both these activities and buying and selling are therefore organized to some extent hierarchically, having a chain of successive agencies lurking behind the retail shop or store. The food that is sold in a grocer's shop goes through many hands before reaching those who consume it, and there is a correspondingly complex organization of auxiliary and supporting services behind most retail agencies. Some degree of interdependence tends to exist among different private service establishments. In a community where automobiles are sold, repair facilities and gasoline are probably available.

Without for the moment going into more detail about the organization of commercial societies in space, we can say that private service enterprises are located close to the consumers—usually in towns and cities—and in suitable proximity to lines of supply from supporting agencies, as well as in association with complementary services.

SETTLEMENTS

WE SHALL REGARD artificial environments now from the standpoint of consumption, and shall consider them as the scene of human want-satisfaction. The notion has already been introduced that human wants include aspirations toward such things as food, clothing, and shelter. Of these wants, those for clothing and food can be satisfied "on the spot" anywhere if certain goods are present; that is, their consumption is not restricted to any particular sort of place, though their production may be. Shelter, however, is provided by more or less durable and substantial facilities. Shelter, particularly residence, therefore, tends to exercise control over the localization of consumption. In all but the most primitive societies some kind of enduring fixed or portable settlement occurs, and consumption is, to a large extent, localized.

The location of settlements responds to a variety of influences. Within the respective territory of any group, settlements are placed as advantageously as possible with respect to natural features. They seek properly drained land, protected spots, positions commanding good communications, and sources of water and fuel not far from the fields or other working places. The house of the Brazilian subsistence homesteader sits amid his crop fields or near them. The Baltic fisherman's house is near his boathouse at the shore. Millions of Asians live on artificial mounds amid the flat and inundated ricefields.

Where natural situations are not suitable, artificial foundations for house sites are sometimes built. The Neolithic lake dwellers of Central Europe constructed their houses on piles, building moveable causeways over the water. The ancient inhabitants of northwest Europe made dikes and mounds and built upon these higher surfaces; whereas peasants of the Mediterranean, and wealthy newcomers to Los Angeles, excavate terraces in the hillsides to build on.

Any settlement, whether it be a lonely hut in the forest or a city of millions of people, is so situated that the means of livelihood are available to its people; in it, they can secure with facility the goods and services of consumption. But while depending on the circumstances, a subsistence farming family must dwell in rather close proximity to its fields, to wells or springs, and to firewood, an urban worker may live very far from clean water supplies, away from any source of fuel, and several thousand miles from the places where his food is grown. Every settlement is connected with appropriate resource sites by definite routes of circulation. In the case of a family band of desert Bushmen, these installations may be only slightly modified natural features which are well known and skillfully used. An Indian village in Mexico may be linked only with facilities disposed over a few dozen or hundreds of square miles, and the whole complex constitutes a miniature universe. The cornfields near the village, the pine forests where the kindling and torches are cut, the grassy glades where roofing material is secured, the hardwood forests from which come house-building materials, the springs, the clay pits for pottery, and the old fields where medicinal plants are gathered constitute the major resource sites and croplands; a network of steep trails connects them with the village, and the individual houses are the combined manufacturing plants and residences of the people, for whom a few services are provided within the village. Left to themselves in this small universe, the people can survive and can even enjoy leisure and small luxuries. In complex exchange economies the scope of organization is much wider. Settlements are closely related to specialized productive features and are diverse in function. Miners build their shacks around the pitheads of mines; loggers build cabins in the forests; farmers construct houses on the land, workers have quarters in the factory towns, and so on. Multiple routes of circulation connect and integrate the settlements. Like the settlements of simpler societies, those in the commercial world are always dependent on and linked to resource sites, cultivated lands, manufacturing plants, and services, regardless of their own specialization. A settlement is always part of a complex of such sites and routes, whatever its scale.

Two kinds of organization of settlements can be distinguished. One, which can be called *homogeneous,* is the form in which, no matter how large the total population, all of the inhabitants are directly supported by the same essential mode of productive activity. Whether a single nuclear family or a population of many thousands is involved, this type of organization is characterized merely by more or less contiguous residence and by social bonds of a non-economic sort. The productive activities of the residents are parallel and unintegrated, or at most are shared through communal working schemes. The various productive units that make up the community are alike and are not specialized for different functions. This kind of settlement may appear either in a "dispersed" form as separate subsistence homesteads or peasant farms, or in an "agglomerated" form as hamlets and villages.

The other kind of settlement is *heterogeneous;* it rests on an economic integration, and its activities are specialized among various constituent units. A number of special occupational groups are represented in the population, and various kinds of productive installations are present. The basis of integration is some form of exchange.[5] Again, the population involved may dwell either in dispersed homes, linked by routes of circulation, or in agglomerated settlements; but, because of technical considerations, the larger part of the people must live in rather immediate reach of the productive installations. The town and city are the typical settlements under this form of organization. We can also list such places as mining camps, loggers' camps, fur-trading posts, and caravan serais, lighthouses, and military outposts as belonging essentially to the integrated kind of settlement pattern; they do not exist except as outposts of large networks of connected sites and routes.

Few humans live totally outside of economic relations with their fellows; the supposed lack of integration of the village is perhaps seldom complete. One commonly finds that there is virtually no trade in the village, but that the peasant does go to market in a neighboring town and in this way is connected with the larger world of commerce, though he lives and works in a homogeneous settlement. The peasant village and the sub-sistence village are therefore of the same distinctive type, though the peasant is transitional economically because he feeds him-self from his own land but also enters trade. A somewhat similar kind of residential settlement is the "dormitory community" of commercial countries whose inhabitants are gathered into an agglomerated settlement away from the scene of their work and possess little or no economic integration. The discriminants con-sidered here are technical and economic, not social; societal unity may be highly developed and many specialized religious and ceremonial roles may be performed within the population of a peasant village or a suburban area. The village is, neverthe-less, different in kind as well as in size from the city.

Settlements may accordingly be classified into *rural* (and suburban) and *urban* ones. Urban settlements, whatever their size, are economically integrated and internally specialized. They may be *agglomerated,* like towns and cities, or *dispersed,* like outposts at particular sites of production. It is clear, then, that the American farm which is highly specialized and inte-grated into the larger economy, and which produces entirely for the market rather than for home consumption, is properly part of a greatly extended urban rather than a rural settlement. This is true with respect to the function of the farm as well as to the style of life of its inhabitants. Life in the suburban countryside, as many of us know, is already rather more bucolic than life on many commercial farms.

Since urban places are differentiated as to the basic functions in which they specialize, it is useful to classify settlements ac-cording to the kind of productive installations with which they are associated, and in which some large portion of their popula-tion is employed. We can recognize 1) settlements around natural resource sites (e.g., mining camps and towns, lumber towns, fishing ports, fur-trading posts). Other settlements are characterized by notable industries, and can be called 2) manu-facturing towns or cities. Places in which wharves, docks, ware-houses, railroad yards, and other transport facilities are concentrated are 3) transport cities. Sometimes a particular service activity completely dominates a settlement in which it is situated, and we can refer to 4) university towns, medical centers, entertainment centers, resorts, administrative centers, and the like. In the vicinity of peasant countrysides there are often 5) market towns, with many specialized functions, to which the village people come to trade.[6]

Needless to say, the urban environment is vastly different from the rural, for in it is always a concentration of services and varied goods. It is a meeting place and melting pot, both a refuge for people and ideas and also a reservoir of new ideas and venturesome populations. It feeds off the land, but nourishes the land with enlightenment and ingenious artifacts. In our world and time, it has begun virtually to absorb the countryside.

The complex communal artifact that is the city becomes a center for certain functions, connected with other central places, and mutually dependent on them. It is bound up in hierarchical orders with other centers by its individual functions; it depends on wholesale service centers for its goods, and on capitals for administration; and it extends its own services to settlements of lower rank. It is an integral part of a larger functioning commercial complex. For the moment we shall postpone discussion of this complex, but we must return to it in Chapter 9.

ORGANIZATION OF ENVIRONMENT

THE FOREGOING OUTLINE of the nature and organization of artificial environments only suggests the peculiarities of man's private self-made world, and the vast number of important problems connected with it. The purpose has been not to lay down final principles of location or to describe fully the kinds of installations built and used by man, but merely to give an idea of these matters that may lead to further thought.

We have suggested that man's artificial environment, in any natural situation and no matter what society is concerned, is an integrated, organized whole. This complex whole is under the influence of natural conditions and of human action, and each of its component parts is influenced by its relations to other parts of the complex. Functionally, the installations of the artificial environment have been classified according to the scheme of: resource sites, circulation routes, manufacturing plants, cultivated lands, service centers, and settlements (the latter overlapping the other categories). To each of these kinds of installations correspond certain distinctive requirements of location in any society.

After this broad outline of artificial environment, we can now proceed to consider the actual ways of livelihood practiced by human groups and the relation of these to societal and economic forms, to techniques and tools, and to particular arrangements of the elements of artificial environments.

CHAPTER EIGHT

WAYS OF
LIVELIHOOD

REGARDLESS of the type of artificial environment they create, all human groups are biologically dependent upon plant and animal populations for their food; thus, they form integral parts of living communities. Men are always symbiotic with certain plants or animals, and the social and economic relationships among men themselves in a society may be recognized also as a kind of symbiosis. The particular character of both kinds of symbiotic relationships has much to do with the spatial order of the human community and with the mode of livelihood manifested in the activity of the human group.[1]

LIVELIHOOD TYPES
AND FOOD-GETTING FORMS

THE FOOD SUPPLY OF MEN must be derived from plants and animals which are either harvested and hunted in the wild or cultivated and raised under domestication. In the first case, natural conditions, in the second, artificial conditions set the spatial pattern that man's activity follows. Peoples who depend upon wild products must gather them where they occur naturally, and peoples with cultivated plants and animals can concentrate their production in fixed plantings or in mobile herds. These possibilities are realized in three of the chief food-getting forms: *nomadic gathering, sedentary cultivation,* and *nomadic pastoralism.* These basic patterns are well known to ethnographers.

Differences among societies in technical level, economy, and social organization, however, are registered in very far-reaching elaborations on the foregoing basic livelihood patterns. Thus, the patterns are differentiated—nomadic gathering proper must be set apart from the skilled and systematic exploitation of a few choice resources with highly developed equipment, and especially from the settled life of some non-cultivating peoples. And groups within each pattern are differentiated—there are many types of cultivation characterized by distinctive facilities and degrees of efficiency.

Another kind of symbiosis, the economic bond, is established in some human groups between food-producers and non-producers of food. This relationship has far-reaching effects upon the spatial order. We have seen that it binds food-producers, usually cultivators, in either facultative (i.e., peasant) or obligate relationships with persons and groups who are obligately dependent on them for food supply. It is under this type of symbiosis that the relation of exchange discussed earlier takes on its great importance; the primary controls on individual livelihood become economic for some or all of the population, rather than strictly ecological, when relations to other persons rather than relations directly to nature govern food supply.

The forms of livelihood organization are congruent with corresponding forms of spatial organization, for both bear on the utilization of dispersed and fluctuating resources. Each livelihood pattern, with its associated spatial order, involves a population group of a certain scale and composition, corresponds to a given economic arrangement, and commands a particular level of technique. When the livelihood of human groups is considered from these several standpoints, and a further distinction is made between those groups that are migratory and those that are sedentary, we can recognize several distinct livelihood types. Let us distinguish seven major categories of livelihood types: *nomadic gathering, nomadic* or *semisedentary predation, semisedentary collecting, shifting* or *sedentary subsistence cultivation, nomadic pastoralism, sedentary peasant cultivation,* and *sedentary commerce.* (Cf. Figure 6.) Admittedly, this terminology leaves much to be desired, but it conforms approximately to habitual usage. Although not all the possible criteria that might be used for classifying livelihood types have been applied here, and the present classification is by no means the only one that could be made, it respects certain obvious and important distinctions.[2]

The food symbiosis is the first consideration here. There are two basic forms of this relation. In one, embracing *gathering, predation,* and *collecting,* humans are obligately dependent on plants or animals, but these organisms are not obligately dependent on man; this is a non-reciprocal relation without domestication. The other form embraces all forms of cultivation and pastoralism and involves domestic organisms which are obligately dependent upon man. The domestic symbiosis is specialized, applying only to a relatively small number of food organisms, while the non-domestic relation can apply to any wild organism. A relatively high degree of specialization on a few species deserves to be set apart as *predation.* We have already distinguished also between systems in which all (or at least all households) of the human society is engaged in food production (subsistence) and systems in which only a portion of the population produces food (exchange). It is also important to distinguish between groups with fixed or portable permanent dwellings and those which are migratory without permanent dwellings. We can also recognize three arrangements in cultivation, depending on the cycle of land use, as intermittent, rotating or permanent cultivation.

In actuality there is a progressive graduation of livelihood forms, both because more than one way of livelihood may be practiced simultaneously by the same group, and because activities and spatial order may vary with the season. Cultivators, pastoralists, and even the urban non-producers of food in full commercial systems, for example, engage in hunting and even in simple gathering on occasion. The same group of people may spend part of the year in the valleys growing crops and part of it tending animals far off in mountain meadows. This is true of mountain folk around the Mediterranean. There are, therefore, many possible and permissible refinements in any livelihood classification; and some of them are suggested in these pages.

LIVELIHOOD TYPES
AND FOOD-GETTING FORMS

I. Food Symbiosis Non-reciprocal (not based upon domestication). Humans obligately symbiotic; plants and animals facultatively symbiotic.

    A. HUMAN GROUP MIGRATORY   TYPES

        1. General symbiosis with numerous plants and animals ....*Gathering*

        2. Specialized symbiosis with a few species of animals ....*Predation*

    B. HUMAN GROUP SEDENTARY, WITH STORAGE ....*Collecting*

II. Food Symbiosis Reciprocal (based upon domestication). Specialized to a few species.

    A. FOOD PRODUCTION GENERAL THROUGHOUT SOCIETY ....(*Subsistence*)

        1. Human group migratory ....*Pastoralism*

        2. Human group sedentary ....*Cultivation*

            a. Land used intermittently ....*—Shifting*

            b. Land used in rotation ....*—Rotating*

            c. Land used continually ....*—Permanent*

    B. FOOD PRODUCTION CONFINED TO A SPECIALIZED GROUP ....(*Exchange*)

        1. Food producers facultatively dependent on non-producers of food; the latter in obligate symbiosis with food-producers ....*Peasantry*

        2. Symbiosis mutually obligate, i.e. reciprocal, between food-producers and non-producers ....*Commerce*

Figure 6

The respective groups assigned here to various livelihood types are very disproportionate numerically. Gatherers, predators, and collectors account for only a few millions of people today; and partially or fully commercial folk make up the great majority of humanity. In the past, of course, the situation was for a long time reversed, for cultivation and urban specialization are relatively recent phenomena.

There is also no particular relation of these livelihood forms to given natural features; isolation and remoteness are the only common characteristics of all the present gatherers' habitats. Scarcely more than a century ago California was a land of collecting folk; now it is all too commercial.

GATHERING

GATHERING PEOPLES are dependent upon the spontaneous productions of their habitats for sustenance. They carry on itinerant hunting and harvesting of wild materials and consume them on the spot. Their working patterns are highly organized, and they follow close schedules in their movements, visiting each resource at the most appropriate time for its use.[3] Their wanderings take place within well-defined territories, like those of animals, and they know and use these territories as efficiently as animals do, discriminating particular sites at particular times for use.

The diagnostic characteristic of the economic system of the gathering groups is the almost complete lack of any spatial segregation of production from consumption activities, and the mobile character of both. Gatherers follow the rhythms of nature and move from place to place, harvesting and consuming whatever is available at the moment. They enjoy little independence from the moods of nature; and, because of their nomadic way of life and lack of means for storing and preserving food and other necessary substances, they are prey to periodic want and material insecurity.

Each territory usually belongs to a small group, seldom over fifty persons, and within it wander smaller bands composed of one or a few families which come together at various times. The territory is inviolable by other members of the same tribe, or linguistic and ceremonial community, and even successful wars do not allow the victors to preempt the losers' lands. Both the schedule of activities and the size of the wandering group are dependent on the season. When food is especially abundant, many of the small bands may come together, as the Ona of Tierra del Fuego do when a whale is stranded; or the Murngin of Australia, when the turtle eggs and the cycads are ready for harvesting. The gathering folk eat voraciously when food is plentiful. Bushmen and Pygmies sit down to consume a whole large animal when they kill one, and the Australians gorge themselves on grubs at certain seasons. In times of dearth the people go for long periods without food.

The exploitation of the habitat by gatherers, like that by animals, is largely concentrated on organic substances. Man, being almost omnivorous, consumes not only game but wild fruits, roots, insect grubs, shellfish, seaweed, fish, and many other things. There are, no doubt, differences in emphasis among different groups. The gathering peoples have a thorough knowledge of the useful properties of things in the world around them, and perhaps know more about edible wild substances than do less primitive folk. The Ona eat the flesh of the guanaco, fox, tuco tuco (a rodent), geese, several kinds of ducks, seals, whales, cormorants, as well as limpets, mussels, crabs, small fish, several fungi, berries, and seeds. The Kalahari Bushmen eat "almost everything that can be eaten": hare, guinea fowl, ostrich, small birds, birds' eggs, fish, anteaters, tortoises, porcupines, snakes, lizards, locusts, scorpions, beetles, young bees, termites, ants' eggs, wild watermelon, sedge roots, berries, various wild roots and fruits, wild figs, palm fruits; they avoid only the meat of the hyena and the baboon.

Despite their recognition of many local resources, however, the gathering peoples can do little to process them. Their techniques are simple, and mostly designed for catching rather than for processing or preserving a food supply. The Bushmen run down game afoot, seeking to tire the animals, to mire them in wet ground, or to drive them into hot dry sands that will sear their hooves. They hunt with well-aimed throwing sticks, poisoned arrows, snares, and concealed pitfalls. Many gathering peoples are highly skilled as trackers, and some are capable of running down and capturing very fleet animals. The power, agility, and endurance of the human body and the quickness of the human wit are used to overpower and outmaneuver animal prey; and the gatherer's intimate familiarity with every crag and corner of the territory assures the utmost care and ability to use whatever plant food becomes available. Gatherers living in dry country, like the Australians, the Bushmen, and the Seri, are aware of every spring and seepage, and are careful to make good provision for a supply of water at all times. They can find water where no one else suspects its presence, and the Bushmen even lay up stores in buried ostrich eggshells as emergency reserves.

The impedimenta of the gatherers include a variety of weapons, like the fifteen-foot spears of the Tasmanians, the bow and arrow of the Negritos and the Seri, the throwing clubs of the Tasmanians and the boomerang of Australians. These peoples also make use of crude stone tools like hammers, axes, awls and scrapers, and of other tools of bone, wood, and shell. All of them use plant fibers and animal skins in various ways, and all make string or cord, which is used for many different purposes, including making nets and snares. Some make rather elaborate basketry.[4]

All the gatherers had the use of fire when discovered by the Whites, though some perhaps did not know how to kindle fire themselves.[5] Some employed burning to condition the native vegetation to produce more edible plants or to drive game. According to early observers, Tasmanians and Bushmen both engaged in burning for these purposes.

The nomadic habit sets limits on the apparatus available for use, since everything must be carried about. For instance, the entire household equipment of an Ona family, sometimes weighing over 200 pounds, is carried in a huge bundle on the woman's back. There is thus little accumulation of heavy equipment among gatherers, and little storage of food materials. Some small amount of game and plant foods may be cached now and then as reserve, and a little food may be carried during treks.

The gathering folk have always tended to make use of whatever products could be acquired without much help from tools and facilities, and most of their resources are things that can be picked up from the ground, plucked from plants, garnered along the seacoast rocks and beaches, or caught in the chase. The artifacts found archaeologically and those recorded among recent gathering peoples are made from such materials as stone, wood, hide, hair, plant fibers, bone, and the like. The resources employed were thus derived almost entirely from plants, animals, and surface minerals. Perhaps a rather extensive catalogue could be made of things made from such readily available resources, and these folk may use to the maximum all the available sorts of materials in their territories; but they have few artificial means of getting at materials buried in the earth, located far out at sea, or otherwise more difficult of access. Except for outcrops of desired kinds of rock, the natural resource sites that they exploit lie wherever wanted plants or animals occur, and so are dispersed throughout the territory of the group. There is little concentration of use on particular sites for more than a short period of harvest, and little of the habitat is neglected.

The artificial features of environment concerned with circulation in these simple societies may include such things as trail markers, territorial boundary markers, lookouts, and signal fires. There are pathways, fords and perhaps bridges of rudimentary construction. Rafts and hollow logs were used in the water by Andamanese and Tasmanians. The circulation routes of gatherers, nevertheless, cannot be very prominent features of the landscape. Since these folk are nomadic, there is practically no development of special sites of manufacture, and, in fact, very little manufacturing at all. Needless to say, there can hardly be any considerable development of service centers, though we may think of cave-shelters sought as refuges, defensive fastnesses, and places where supernatural forces are especially potent, as akin to such sites.

The gatherer's dwelling is a simple affair, seldom more than a temporary lean-to of brush, covered with boughs, skins, or bark. It often falls to the woman to prepare the lean-to for the family. Some few groups, when first visited, lived in caves during the course of their wanderings; but most were on the move all year round, and seldom stayed in one spot for more than a few days. For reasons of sanitation, if for no other, they had to leave the littered and dirty campsite after a short time.

True gatherers are few in modern times, though at one time all men must have been gatherers. Through most of Paleolithic time the human species must have lived a nomadic life much like that of animals, except for the possession of tools, and speech and fire, which are features of the peculiar social and cultural habits of man. The gatherers of recent times are the Ona, Yahgan, and Alacaluf of Tierra del Fuego; the Goajiro, Guajibo, Abipones, and Botocudo of tropical South America; the Chiricahua of the southwestern United States; the Bushmen of South Africa; the aboriginal Australians; the Negritos of Malaya and the Philippines; some hardly-known forest and mountain peoples of Upper Burma, Thailand, Indo-China, Indonesia, and New Guinea; and the native Tasmanians, as well as a few other peoples like these. Many of these peoples are already extinct, or on the verge of extinction. Only the Pygmies of tropical Africa appear to have maintained their numbers fairly well.

All the gathering peoples, few and primitive, have suffered catastrophe when they met the expanding Whites, Bantu and Orientals. The dismal story, everywhere repeated, is of incomprehension and hostility between them and the newcomers, and of eventual degradation and extinction of the native gatherers.[6]

The habitats of recent gathering peoples have been the most remote and inaccessible corners of the world, but in ancient times similar folk must have wandered over more prodigal countries. The Ona, for example, live in the cold turfland and stunted beechwoods of southernmost South America; the Bushmen, Seri, Chiricahua, and many of the Australians in bleak deserts; the Botocudo, Pygmies, and Negritos in the deep tropical forests; and the Tasmanians on a temperate isle, lost in the southern seas. We can, therefore, make few generalizations as to the kind of physical environments the gatherers inhabit, but can suppose that at one time they inhabited all kinds.

The gatherers work hard. They are almost constantly preoccupied, according to all accounts, with the search for food. There is little opportunity for innovation in their societies, since mistakes can easily be fatal, and time is scarce. Lacking any very elaborate apparatus, the gatherers have slight means of improving upon nature by invention, or of improving upon existing techniques by combining and extending them. Their nomadic life, their immediate dependence on the wild habitat, their lack of storage and processing facilities, their poor stock of portable tools, their low density of population and small social groups, and their compulsory absorption in an eternal round of foraging, preclude much leisure, luxury, or innovation, and make their societies rather inflexible.

The gatherers are at the mercy of the seasons. Often, too, they are also at the mercy of hostile, exploitative and better-equipped neighbors. It is no wonder that the gathering groups are now mostly extinct or moribund, but it is indeed a great wonder that humanity ever got beyond this trying and confining way of life.

Estimates of the population of gathering peoples and of the extent of territory they occupy are few. The former population of Tasmania, for instance, has been estimated at from 500 to as many as an unlikely 20,000 persons. The best authorities give around 2,000, in a total area of some 26,000 square miles. Aboriginal Tasmania must, therefore, have had a density of population of about one person for ten square miles. This figure takes into account all of the territory available no matter how little used; for density can only be estimated justly by accounting for the deliberately neglected, as well as the successfully exploited, land involved.

The Kalahari Bushman band of from 100 to 150 persons has a traditional territory whose size averages perhaps 700 square kilometers, or about one person for three square miles. The Ona, numbering some 3,500 persons around 1850, occupied a part of Tierra del Fuego totalling about 10,000 square miles; there were 39 territories within this area, each belonging to one large extended family. The density among the Ona was thus around one person for three square miles.

Since gatherers are widely dispersed in space and moving

constantly from place to place, they are able to have little impact on their natural surroundings. Scarcely able to command any of the processes of nature, except fire—which may not always have been at their disposal—the gatherers may have been effective chiefly in such simple ways as the dissemination of seeds from fruits that they consumed, the slight reduction of animal populations through their hunting and trapping, the occasional serious disturbance of vegetation around camps, and the like. The simpler gatherers' activities influence the plant world mainly at one period in the life cycle of each species: when the fruit is ready for dispersal or the roots are in condition to be dug. The gathering of fruits and the scattering of some portion of them into spots where they may germinate may actually be favorable to the plant species. During most of the life history of the plant, human action does not affect it at all. Similarly, much of the food of gatherers consists of terrestrial or marine invertebrates, many of which are consumed only in the late stages of maturity. Thus, they may interfere very little with the reproduction of the species. The larger animals are not only not completely at the mercy of the small bands of gatherers, but may, on the contrary, prey on them. The total effect of the simplest gathering groups on the other organisms of their habitat is very slight; they do little either to help or to hinder the life around them. Their modification of inorganic features of environment is even less. Man as a gatherer is not yet fully dominant in nature.

COLLECTING AND PREDATION

MANY PEOPLES are or were semi-nomadic. This type has some sort of fixed settlements from which, or sometimes carrying which, they wander for part of the year or for short periods. Some of these peoples, indeed, are much like the gatherers except that they possess permanent dwellings or portable camps. Others, however, differ from them in a fundamental way: they transport raw materials to special sites, usually in or near their dwellings, and store them there, sometimes after performing some simple manufacturing operations on them. We must, therefore, differentiate the nearly-nomadic peoples who, like the Andamanese, the Yukagir, and the Paiute, must be considered fundamentally wanderers and do not or did not collect or process materials to any great extent, from the mainly sedentary folk who regularly inhabit—or at least return periodically to —a home base in which they store material, and those semi-nomads with elaborate but portable camps, like the Indians of the Plains. Thus the real division between gatherers and collectors is on the basis of storage, and manufacture is closely connected with it.

Collecting here denotes the economic-technical form of peoples who have no domestic plants or animals and engage in little or no regular commerce, but possess permanent structures, fixed or portable, in which they manufacture and store materials. Collecting peoples may be divided into three kinds, according to the primary sources of their livelihood: 1) those who specialize, like the Tlingit and Kwakiutl, in exploiting rich resources of fish and other sea life; 2) those who, like the Aleut, hunt sea mammals, or, like the Plains Sioux, hunt land mammals; 3) and those who efficiently and intensively harvest the seeds and roots of plants, as did most of the tribes of California. To be sure, the hunters knew plant foods, the fishers used vegetable material and game, and the seed-collecting Pomo of California hunted deer and fished in Clear Lake, but the staple supplies of the respective groups set them apart. The techniques of these peoples were or are very well suited to the exploitation of their particular environments, which provide a few rich resources.

With respect to mobility there are two kinds of groups here, one basically sedentary and the other migratory. The sedentary folk or *collectors proper* exploit sea-life, plant substances and small game located within one territory, and accumulate and elaborate the supplies they gather in a fixed settlement. The migratory people or *predatory* groups are hunters of land or sea animals who follow their quarry as predators on the herd, and carry with them their portable dwelling facilities, usually tents, as well as a considerable array of weapons and other tools, and supplies of food.

The *predatory* groups mostly wander in a vast territory, following the animals that are moving in their regular migratory cycle over the land or along the shores of the sea. The encounters of the hunters with various species of their prey come at different times, depending on the habits of the animals. The arctic shore hunters may pursue walrus at one season, seals at another, and whales at yet another; and inland hunters may follow the wild caribou part of the year and encamp along the rivers to fish for salmon at the season of the run. Each migratory group tends to claim particular territories, hunting sites, or herds of animals as its own.

Among sedentary collecting folk, work is carried on in a limited territory traditionally assigned to the local settlement, within which individuals may also have exclusive claim to such resources as the acorns of particular oaks or to special fishing sites. The fishing posts among the Columbia River peoples are individual properties. The family or group of families following a seasonal cycle of activities engages in hunting, fishing, harvesting, and the processing of goods. The peoples of the American Northwest Coast dry salmon and other fish over their house-fires; the California Pomo women grind acorns to meal on stone mortars, and leach out the bitterness of the meal. Besides the preparation and the preservation of foodstuffs, the collectors typically engage in many other kinds of manufacture. They prepare skins and sew clothing of them; carve ivory, wood or stone containers and ornaments; build sometimes elaborate dwellings, boathouses and ceremonial buildings; and make canoes and boats of planks, hides or rushes. The boats of the Aleuts and Eskimo are as good or better for their purposes, it is said, than any other ever made, and the baskets of the California Indians are the best of their kind.

The materials gathered in the wild, that is "produced," are collected for consumption in the dwelling place. The spatial segregation of production from consumption, and the partial division of societal roles into specialized activities, begin to appear among collectors. Collecting peoples, and the specialized predator groups exhibiting the same kind of organization, tend to live in permanent villages or temporary camps consisting of a number of distinct households or consumption units.

Division of labor is typical not only within the family unit, as among gatherers, but also to some extent within the settlement as a whole. In the camps of the Eskimo, the rancherias of the Californians, and the villages of the Haida, specialists perform skilled functions for all the settlement. There are shamans and scouts, boat-builders and dance leaders. There is little real exchange, however, because the work of these specialists is destined mainly for communal, not individual, use and benefit; what exchange exists is likely to be of the "reciprocity" variety.

Division of labor is customary in food-getting. The Pomo women gather certain grass seeds, the men hunt rabbits and deer, and both sexes work together to harvest the acorn crop. Among the Kwakiutl and their neighbors, women gather berries and cedar bark and the men fish. The Eskimo woman is almost a "housewife" in the American sense; she sits at home with the domestic chores while the husband hunts.

Collectors possess a wider variety of implements than do gatherers, such as more highly perfected weapons, leather- and wood-working tools, and so on. They also have a number of machines, but are especially distinguished by their wealth of buildings, tents, traps, boxes, boats, sleds and other apparatus of the kind we have called "facilities." Not only does the possession of these artifacts make possible more efficient hunting, fishing, and havesting, but also certain of them enable the collectors to transport goods over land or water, and even to wander freely without surrendering their advantage of accumulated stores and equipment. The possession of buildings and containers is also important for the processing and preservation of foodstuffs and the manufacture of other goods.

The resource sites frequented by collectors and predators are perhaps in general more specialized than those of the gatherers. These peoples continue to make use of the same products, but in addition are able to acquire materials more skillfully, through such techniques as fishing, trapping and even mining, and to employ a greater variety of materials in manufacturing. A great number of natural materials is in use among both sedentary collectors and the wandering predators, and the uses to which they put materials are definitely specialized. The preparation of complex foodstuffs, the use of special kinds of wood, stone, bone, or ivory for the decorative arts; the selection of plant fibers for baskets; and the use of wood and other materials for boat- and house-building; the use of mineral pigments for personal ornamentation; and other such traits mark the collectors and the predators as discriminating, intensive and skillful users of resources. Specialized resource sites are commonly found where exploitation is concentrated on certain choice fishing grounds, hunting tracts, deposits of salt, ochre, magnesite, obsidian, and other minerals, and harvesting grounds for particular seeds and fruits. The natural resource sites of the collectors and predators tend to be well localized, persistently and amply used, and often are even held in the possession of particular individuals or groups in the community.

These folk still do not mingle much with strangers, and their lines of communication are not much elaborated, though well-defined trails can sometimes still be recognized in places where such peoples have lived. They do, however, possess efficient means of transport like the great canoes of Melanesia and northwest America, the baidarkas and kayaks of the American Arctic, the dogsled and dog-travois of interior North America, the reed balsa of California, the skis and snowshoes of northern Eurasia, and so on. These vehicles, craft, and gear provide improved means of transporting goods, as well as of travel.

Collectors tend to practice manufacture in their settlements, where goods are stored. The dwelling is employed as the workshop for food processing, tool-making, preparation of clothing, the creation of ornaments, and other artistic production. Some persons may engage in highly specialized production during part of the time, and may make ornaments, weapons, ceremonial regalia, boats, and such things in their dwellings. Certain communities may be noted for a particular kind of manufactures, as some of the Pomo settlements were for their magnesite work, the Chumash villages of southern California were for their soapstone bowls, and some Eskimo camps are for ivory carving.

There is no general exchange pattern, and so such manufactures are of limited importance, and full-time manufacturing plants are not found.

In collecting and predatory societies certain places begin to be set aside as service centers. The settlements of many peoples of this kind in Asia and America are characterized by the presence of sweathouses; dance-houses or dance-floors; and sometimes monuments, like the grave-posts of the Amur country and the totem pole of northwestern America. There are also particular persons who have unusual powers which gain them the respect and awe of their neighbors, and who practice wizardry and medicine, as well as leading ritual. These "shamans" provide a kind of semi-public services. Again the warriors, often a group apart with their own leadership, are a service group. Warriors and shamans may even live apart from their fellows. Thus a number of places are distinguished on occasion as sites for particular services, and there are persons present in at least some of these societies with special service functions.

The peoples whom we class as collectors and predators are chiefly found in northeastern Asia and northwestern North America, as far as California and the Plains. The collecting kind of life was clearly much more widespread formerly, and was probably characteristic of the so-called Upper Paleolithic and Mesolithic in general. The recent concentration, or survival, of collectors around the northern Pacific is undoubtedly best explained by peculiar historical circumstances, and notably by the incomplete diffusion of cultivation, rather than by any distinctive feature of environment. Yet the environment cannot be overlooked. Particular features of these countries were especially well suited to the kinds of exploitation practiced by the collectors and the predatory hunters and fishers. How different their resources were from those formerly found in other areas, and how much human activity had to do with them, cannot be estimated.

The rhythm and volume of consumption among the collectors and predators no longer need reflect directly the seasonal or momentary states of nature. Production is, however, still dependent on the cycles of plant and animal activity. The hunters, fishermen and plant collectors are limited in their harvest of the respective resources upon which they depend by seasonal cycles of nature, as are the simple gatherers. The salmon run in the rivers around the North Pacific for only a few weeks out of the year, and the Kamchadal or Chinook salmon-fishermen had to extract their annual supply of fish by working day and night; the Indians of the Central Valley of California similarly had but a few weeks to gather in the crop of wild grass seeds. However, these and other collecting peoples could preserve the plant and animal foods thus gathered and make them serve throughout the year, or at least for many months. Production is dependent on the seasons and the whims of nature still, but consumption is equalized over a longer period. The techniques of preservation and storage of food, and the elaborate preparation of food for use, are basic to this more stable and settled mode of life.

The life of the collectors is correspondingly much less rigorous and exposed to accident than that of the gatherers. We see in their religion, social organization, art, and warfare evidence enough of this. Some collector communities, like those of the Northwest Coast, have been large settlements of several hundred people. They often have a large oral literature, a system of social classes or something like it (in some cases), elaborate traditions of warfare, and highly developed arts. Among some peoples of the Northwest Coast the potlatch, a conspicuous and wanton destruction of individual wealth to enhance prestige, was formerly practiced. The folktales even of the poorer peoples of this type are impressive, and Eskimo ivory carving, Northwest carved stone and woodwork, and California baskets and featherwork testify to the well-elaborated artistic traditions that had arisen among collectors, as well as the availability of leisure for creative activities.

The spatial mobility of collectors is less rigidly limited than that of gatherers. The Haida and Kwakiutl had time and means to make war on their neighbors, and the Pomo to wander as shamans and even traders. The regularity of the yearly cycle still imposes itself, but there is more flexibility in the choice of activities during most of the year than among gatherers. Interchange with neighbors is possible, and one group borrows occasional ideas from another. Experimentation and innovation, too, probably become more frequent.

The collectors, though limited still to the exploitation of the spontaneous productions of nature, command means of doing so efficiently enough to specialize in a few especially rewarding uses of their time and effort, and to employ specialized and ingenious techniques. Their economies exhibit a much greater selectivity in resource use than do those of gatherers. At the same time they release themselves from full dependence upon the momentary state of nature by modifying goods through manufacture and storing them for future need. The accumulation of capital in sedentary locations or portable camps, the storage of consumer goods, the concentration on particular kinds of production, the increased leisure and mobility of these peoples promote greater intercourse—not always friendly— among different groups, and greater development of resources, skills and artifacts. Work can be invested in new productive facilities such as storage places, baskets, tools, boats, fishing gear, weapons, and the like. People can sometimes change their techniques or discover new resources. Quite dense local populations are maintained, and leisure is abundant enough for many more activities besides those connected directly with livelihood to make their appearance.

There are, however, times of crisis and catastrophe among the collecting peoples when the game disappears or the seed-harvest fails. Sometimes in the past hunting peoples have been guilty of overexploitation of game. This is conceivably the reason for the disappearance of horses, camels and elephants from North America, and of many other large mammals from other places in the world in fairly late times.

Collectors and predators achieve substantial modification of their habitat, doubtlessly sometimes to their own detriment. On the whole, however, they possess efficient techniques of exploitation which need not lead to their ruin. Changes brought about by contact with outsiders, however, have resulted in deterioration of habitats. When firearms became available to the Eskimo they were welcomed, but the game soon began to disappear.

Complex changes in social organization and in working habits also result from close contact with strangers. Some of the factors in the decay, downfall, and extinction of simpler societies have surely been traceable to the presence of newcomers and the demoralization and disorganization that resulted from it.[7] The willingness to work may fail, or the necessary cycle of the old production system may be broken when the "native" goes to work for the stranger. The invading Whites have seldom respected the territorial structure of native communities, and have deprived the gatherers and the collectors of the means of gaining livelihood by the old way of life. Some native groups, like the Plains Indians, have fought back fiercely. Others, though treated perhaps with more benevolence by missionaries or settlers, usually have declined in the long run. The forests are cut, the rivers dammed; the old harvesting and hunting territories become the cultivated fields and pastures of the strangers.

One result of the decay of the old collecting communities is that many areas formerly inhabited are now desolate, and old resources are now almost unused. Mountain, desert, forest, and seacoast lands that used to support modest populations are at present left unexploited, or seldom used. In places cattle and sheep have replaced men as the dominant inhabitants of these lands, especially in mountain and desert country.

Most of the collectors and predatory hunters and fishers around the North Pacific have either disappeared before the march of Western and Oriental high cultures, or have been incorporated into the advancing societies of the newcomers and have given up the old way of life. In 1800 there were at least two million people living as collectors and hunters or fishers in this area, and a few more elsewhere (Chaco, Amazon, India). Kroeber estimates a density over the whole Pacific coast area of North America north of Mexico, in primitive times, at a little over one person per two square miles (25.2 per 100 km.^{2}), with a maximum density of over one and a half persons for a square mile on the lower Columbia, and an average of around one per square mile in California.[8] The decline of the larger concentrations was catastrophic during the nineteenth century, as S. F. Cook has shown.[9]

The chief effect of collecting peoples on the world around them comes from the continuous inroads that they make on the plant and animal populations on which their livelihood depends. Perhaps this is not simply a negative influence, for the curtailment of population increase among animal species may preserve a healthy balance between the animals' numbers and their food supply. Similarly, the harvest and transport of seeds for food may favor the dispersal and increase of certain plants. The use of fire has been another means of environmental modification. No one knows yet what part artificially induced fires may have played in changing landscapes in the more distant past, but documentation is abundant for its recent use and wide effects. Probably almost all present vegetations have at one time or another been modified by fire or other man-induced effects, some of which were contributed by past gatherers and collectors. It has even been suggested that some or all the grasslands of the world developed under repeated burnings promoted by man.[10] The effects of this and other practices can only be a subject of speculation in the present state of knowledge.

CULTIVATION

CULTIVATION introduces new relationships into man's ecology. The livelihood systems of cultivation are based upon a particular form of symbiosis between men and plants. In it man's work provides an artificial environment for the plants he depends on. Two new features characterize the ecological relations of the cultivating peoples. First, the period of human interference with the plant is extended far beyond the fructifying stage and comes to include the entire life cycle. Second, man interferes purposively with the soil and water regime, and becomes concerned with microclimates.

Cultivation implies the planting, protection and nurturing of desired species. Man concerns himself with the selection of reproductive material—seeds or clone shoots—and with affording proper conditions for germination, establishment, and vegetative growth, and usually flowering and fruiting. Each of these phases of plant care has its own requirements.

The term *cultivation* applies, strictly speaking, to what is done on a restricted plot of ground, and to the things growing on it. As a form of production it is intensely localized. Its sites are permanent or at least perennial. They commonly adjoin the sites of storage, manufacture, and consumption used by those who cultivate.

The *farm* is thus the scene of both production and consumption activities. It very often consists of the dwellings of the cultivator, his workshops, gardens, granaries, and fields. Where a settled group of cultivators lives together in a village or hamlet, the settlement itself is commonly placed amidst the fields its people till. At times the fields may lie away at a distance, but they are an inseparable part of the village universe of everyday.

One man can only tend a certain area of ground or a certain number of plants, but land suitable for cultivation usually occurs in larger contiguous tracts than one man and his family can work. For this reason, if for no other, cultivators are likely to be gregarious. They are also motivated to protect the gardens and livestock from wild animals, or the granaries from thieves. Perhaps the most important reason is reliance on societal means of carrying on ritual activities, and of transmitting and arbitrating all the complexities of culture.

Cultivators tend to live in settlements of many families, among whom may be specialists in ritual, learning, and material skills essential to the work of the people. Even where so-called "shifting cultivation" is practiced, these settlements maintain themselves in one place for long periods, as among the Mayan-speaking peoples of Guatemala and southern Mexico, and many of the hill people of southeastern Asia. This is true even though the forest lands that can be cleared for fields and which supply the necessary firewood, and the water sources, lie at considerable distances from the village.

The schedule of the work of cultivators is a yearly round of different activities carried on primarily in one restricted locality, the field or garden. The cycle of climate and the life cycle of the plants establish the program of the cultivator's efforts, which are intended to promote the best development of the crops at each ecological stage. The nature of the tasks varies with the season, but the locale is always the same. Different operations are carried on to condition the soil, to clear a surface, to modify the growth form of the plants, to combat pests. Different auxiliary substances are brought to the site of the plantings to aid the growth of the crop, like water and materials that enrich the soil. Thus, throughout the growing season the cultivator's activity is concentrated, in time and space, upon the place where his crop stands; his work is extremely localized, though varied. Usually, but not always, his dwelling is in close proximity to the land he cultivates. The only errands that may regularly take him further from his cropland are the search for firewood and other forest materials, the hauling of water, and the hunt.

The spatio-temporal pattern of cultivation is essentially the same for all sorts of crop growing, horticultural or agricultural, under both subsistence and exchange economies.[11] The farmer's work is everywhere bound to site and season. The cultivator has to be sedentary, but the relative permanence of his settlement depends upon the kind of farming he practices. There is a great difference between several sorts of cultivation, which can be called *permanent, rotating,* and *intermittent.* A field, and even more a garden, can be used year in, year out for crops, if by some means its fertility is maintained. Fields may be left fallow periodically for a year or more to permit natural restoration of their fertility, with or without artificial fertilization and cover crops; or fields may be carved out of forest and brush land for a few years, then allowed to revert to the wild condition.

The *permanent* use of land is restricted, though, to places where the soil can be renewed regularly by heavy additions of nutrients, and protected from destruction caused by running water and other agencies. Large installations for water control, constructed with a great expenditure of labor, are in some places associated with permanent farming. With effective control of water supply, ample supplements of nutrients to the soil, and intensive use of labor, certain kinds of permanent croplands commonly furnish high yields and support dense rural populations. This situation prevails most notably in the countries of the Far East and parts of Europe. In the places where permanent cultivation is most practiced, the technical equipment associated with it consists of elaborate facilities, rather simple tools, and a few unpowered machines.

Perhaps the simplest form of permanent cultivation is that which is dependent upon natural replenishment of the soil of streambeds. Peoples like the tribes of the Colorado and some of East Africa utilize streambeds for growing crops during low-water season, after the annual floods have deposited a fresh layer of silt. In eastern and southern Asia, farmers go to an opposite extreme, and make entirely artificial diked enclosures, in which water stands for long periods over an impermeable soil pan. Into this "tank," fertilizers are often introduced, and these enclosed pond-fields may be utilized for centuries virtually without rest, since their fertility is constantly being renewed. The wet-rice complex is associated closely with such pond-fields.[12]

The landscape most closely identified with lowland rice cultivation of this kind is of course that typical in China, Japan, Luzon or Java, where practically the entire lowland surface is made up of a checkerboard of rice fields separated by "bunds" of earth, sometimes planted with trees or crops. This is undoubtedly one of the most stable geographic systems integrating human activity in nature. In places in China, the wet rice landscape is so ancient and so unbroken that it has been almost impossible to reconstruct the picture of the landscape from before it was established.

The *rotating* use of land is characterized by the temporary withdrawal of fields from cultivation during a cycle of two or three years, or by the alternation of various crops in successive years in the same field. (This term thus includes fallowing here.) The fields are laid out in a permanent arrangement, but their use varies from time to time. There is typically less assiduous attention to artificial water supply and artificial supplementing of fertilizer under this form of cultivation than under the preceding, though newer practices are tending to eliminate this difference.

Whereas the most common source of energy in the permanent cultivation of the Far East is human and animal muscle power, in rotating cultivation it is commonly mostly draft animals that furnish power, and later, in its most modern form, this kind of farming employs power machines. With the use of machines, including efficient irrigation pumps and fertilizer factories, rotating cultivation tends to approach a permanent state. The crops, under its most advanced forms, are still rotated to avoid excessive strain on the soil, but there is no longer any need of fallowing when soil fertility can be supplemented and texture and structure can be restored through the use of artificial products, by a mixed-farming complex with livestock, and by machines.

In almost all of Europe, in a large part of the Near East, India and North Africa, and in the overseas lands where Europeans have settled, the rotating cultivation that is the modern descendant of ancient Mesopotamian small-grain agriculture is found. With it are associated the plow and draft animals, and nowadays also much machinery. Under this kind of agriculture, lands of level to moderately rolling relief which may be either irrigated or non-irrigated are used. Not only fields, but orchards, vineyards, and gardens, most especially in their Mediterranean forms, are worked. Rotating cultivation is the chief kind of commercial agriculture.

The farmers of Western plowfield agriculture prepare their fields anew each year, commonly tilling them clean and plowing several times. Only one crop occupies the field, as a rule. The soil surface may be left uncovered for several months out of the year, or may be occupied by cover crops to restore the soil.

The third type, *intermittent* or shifting cultivation,[13] consists in clearing natural vegetation cover from the land, using it for crop-growing for a few years, and abandoning it once more to natural growth once its fertility has dropped far enough. Intermittent cultivation requires a large amount of land, for if the cycle from clearing to abandonment of a plot is only three or four years, and the time required for the recuperation of the plot is several times as long, the ratio of abandoned and recuperating land to that under cultivation at any one time may be as high as five or ten to one. This form of cultivation is practiced, of course, with little use of elaborate facilities, because of its temporary character in any given spot. Even the living sites of the cultivators may be changed from time to time to accommodate to shifts in the location of the fields, so dwellings are fairly simply constructed. Ordinary implements, rather than machines, are commonly employed, and human rather than animal or inanimate power is mostly used.

One important feature of intermittent cultivation is the phenomenon known as "hiving-off" of settlements. When a local population dependent on a limited area of land becomes too dense, individuals and groups of persons may move away some considerable distance and found new settlements and clear new lands. This pioneering is still an integral part of the system in places like southern Mexico and Guatemala; the White pioneers of woodland North America practiced the same thing. It may have existed since early times, and probably "shifting cultivation" has had a lot to do with the spread of human population about the world.

The crop assemblages of the shifting cultivators everywhere seem to include staple items that can be carried about and planted in pure stands. Often the few seed crops of predominantly root-growing areas are associated with uplanders who move about and change their clearings from time to time, while the root growers remain fixed in their lowland sites. In the New World, at least, seed crops seem to be hill crops to a large degree, though not all hill crops are seed-propagated. Seed crops are easily transported, and most of them produce food within one season, so that they allow of great mobility, combined with more security and abundance than the gatherers or collectors can usually enjoy. Peoples who grow seed crops are still expanding in such places as southeastern Mexico, the highlands of Laos, and Ethiopia, by means of the periodic hiving off of shifting-cultivator communities.

Intermittent cultivation is now characteristic mostly of the intertropical regions, though formerly it was practiced widely in northern temperate lands. There are vestiges of it in Finland

and Russia, Korea and Japan, the Carpathians, and even the United States, and historical evidence exists for its presence over a much larger area in the past.

The artificial installations characteristically found in association with cultivation—natural resource sites, circulation routes, manufacturing plants, cultivated lands, service centers, and settlements—are obviously extremely diverse, and the spatial orders that they constitute are exceedingly varied. Only their most general features, and the major differences associated with the several chief forms of cultivation, can be considered here. Five broad classes of farming stand out: 1) intermittent subsistence cultivation of seed and root crops—shifting slash-and-burn cultivation—now found mostly in hilly country and forest lands of the tropics;[14] 2) permanent subsistence horticulture,[15] using simple tools and human muscle-power and growing largely root-crops, in scattered locations in the tropics (e.g., Melanesia, the Caribbean, Guinea);[16] 3) permanent peasant agriculture with a horticultural component, employing some animal power and using tools, some machines, and elaborate facilities, growing rice and many auxiliary crops, found mostly in East and South Asia; 4) rotating peasant agriculture, sometimes with horticultural elements, using animal power, tools and machines, and sometimes using irrigation facilities, growing primarily small grains, pulses, and other seed crops, and found over the Middle East, North Africa, Mediterranean Europe, Central Asia, North China, and western India;[17] 5) the commercial rotating agriculture of Europe and culturally related lands, with power machines and complex facilities, growing small grains and a great variety of other crops, and associated with animal husbandry.[18]

The detailed description of the artificial features associated with these cultivation systems, some of which have very complex "cultural landscapes," must be left to the regional geography of the respective countries. Ignoring the countless lesser differences traceable to historical and contemporary distinctiveness of cultures, social organization, economic systems, and technique, the several complexes stand well apart.

The utilization of resources among intermittent subsistence cultivators is hardly much advanced over what is found among collectors. The artifacts of these folk are objects of wood, stone, bone, plant fibers, and so on. They exploit the surface minerals and the products of the forest and the seacoast, but cannot effectively exploit mineral raw materials and fuels at any depth; metals are scarce among them. Favorite hunting and fishing spots and gathering grounds, some readily-worked shallow beds of clay or seams of rock, and similar natural resource sites supply their needs. Lacking vehicles and draft animals almost entirely, and not dependent on exchange, subsistence farmers, like collectors, seldom develop routes of circulation any more elaborate than trails. Their manufactures are performed at home, but often special equipment is used. In the weaving of cloth, pottery-making, woodcarving and carpentry, food-preservation, and other manufactures, the loom, the potter's wheel, woodworking tools, and so on are employed; but special facilities are seldom needed to house these activities. The cultivated patches of shifting agriculture occupy scattered clearings in forest or brush, and are very often cluttered with the remains of trunks and stumps. The planting of crops irregularly among these relics gives the plot a disorderly appearance, and sometimes it is half-filled with weeds and renascent wild growth along with the crops. The crops themselves may be mixed: maize, squash, pole- or bush-beans and an assortment of small things like peppers, tomatoes, and gourds are planted in the same clearing in Central America and Mexico. The plot may be located in a valley bottom or on a steep hill slope; because of the tools used, extremely precipitous hillsides can be planted.[19] The scattered distribution of the slash-and-burn system amid many kinds of natural environments allows no single generalization about the location of its fields.

Intermittent subsistence cultivators are by definition rustic people, and they tend to live in hamlets and small villages, or in isolated huts. Again, generalization is impossible here. Within their settlements, whether dispersed or agglomerated, there may be certain service centers having to do with ceremonial and political life. In no case can the settlements be called urban, though, for services are few and specialization is very slight.

The common features that the traveler might expect to find

in a country occupied by intermittent subsistence cultivators, whether located in Amazonian Brazil, upland Assam, the hills of Nigeria, the forested river plains of Sumatra, or western Madagascar, would be many. The vegetation would be a patch-work of stands of different heights and of rather different species-composition, and would include tangles of vine and brush and weedy openings; here and there would be en-countered a cultivated plot, in which maize, rice, millet, yams, bananas, beans, manioc, or other crop-plants were growing without order amid logs and charred stumps or standing naked trunks. Around the plots there might be rude fences of brush or poles or spiny branches.

A trail winding through forest and across open grassy places would eventually lead the traveler to a group of rustic struc-tures covered with thatch roofs of grass or palm, standing in a dry expanse of naked earth littered with refuse on which wan-dered fowl, dogs, pigs, and children. The buildings might be many, forming a small village, or only the few belonging to an isolated homestead. In the Americas, there might be a plaza and a whitewashed church and civil agency; in the East a temple; in Africa a mud-walled chief's compound. The men might all be in the fields; the women would glide timidly into the dark house interiors, the children would run away, the lean dogs yap and slink off. Passing onward, the traveler would find water-pits at the nearby ford, cavities in the streambanks where clay had been scooped out, piles of firewood along the trail waiting to be carried home to the village. He could walk thus for many days and find things always much the same, ex-cept that people's dress, the shape of the roofs, the decoration on the pots might vary from place to place.

Unlike intermittent cultivation, subsistence horticulture in-volves the use of permanent or perennial plots on which great labor is expended. The resource sites are of the same nature as those of intermittent cultivators, because the technical equip-ment of both kinds of folk is similar. Metals are hardly known. Clay, shell, wood, bark, hide, fibers, stone, and bast are used in simple manufactures, mostly carried on in the house and its yard or the village common ground. Since these folk are settled,

the houses may be more elaborately built, boats may be beauti-
fully carved and well made, the communal cult may occupy a
large and imposing structure, and storehouses for food may be
in evidence. Routes of circulation are no more developed than
among shifting cultivators, though the trails may be more worn,
and exotic weeds may line them. The canoes along the beach
betoken voyaging, however. The people live again in villages,
in which the ceremonial buildings, the boat-builder's stand on
the beach, the charms attached to trees and granaries and houses,
attest to the presence of some specialized services. The cultivated
lands, apart from the great fruit and shade trees planted around
the village, lie a short distance away. They are composed of
many small contiguous plots, neatly tended, in which grow
yams, manioc, bananas, ginger, taro, sweet-potatoes and other
crops. They are well cleared and cleaned. Around them, the
uneven development of different stands of brush and forest
testifies to past planting on other, nearby lands. Not far distant
lie several other villages with their gardens.

The same sort of landscape, with some minor modifications,
might be observed in Polynesia, New Guinea, Melanesia, Micronesia, and various parts of Indonesia, on the shores of the Gulf
of Guinea, in southern Ethiopia, in eastern Panama, and here
and there around the Caribbean and in the interior of South
America. In the highlands of Peru, something not unlike it,
though more bleak and poor in appearance, would be found. In
many places the shifting pattern coexists with sedentary horticulture in the same general area. The well-tilled neat gardens and
the substantial villages of the horticulturists, usually in the lower
country, mark their lands apart from those of the less settled
intermittent hill cultivators; in social life and custom the horticulturists are far different, having complex communal organization and ceremonial life.

Some of the peoples living in the districts named and under
the conditions described may well be counted as peasants, for
some of them engage in a certain amount of trade (in addition
to the reciprocal exchange common among many of the horticulturists.) The landscapes occupied by peasants, therefore,
grade off from these. Among peoples who enter into substantial

relations with outsiders through trade, however, there are additional features in the landscape of artificial origin.

Most peasant peoples know the use of metals, make and use various machines, and consume commodities brought from a distance. Special resource sites are intensively worked; roads run through the countryside and carry a traffic of goods and people. There are market towns and cities with specialized workshops and stores and many service centers, or at least elaborate periodic markets in which many goods and services are offered. The land is cleared extensively and the fields stretch continuously for great distances.

The Oriental forms of peasant landscapes are full of busy people and their handiwork. The hills are usually still in forest, but the lowlands are filled with rice fields, banked and flooded, and the lower slopes are often terraced. Roads cross the countryside, as well as canals and ditches. Here and there is a mine, a quarry, a kiln, a saltworks. Clumps of trees or giant bamboos signify isolated homesteads with sturdy houses and outbuildings, or mark the presence of villages. Kitchen gardens surround the dwellings, or occupy some part of the fields. In the towns and cities periodic markets are often held, and there are temples and administrative buildings, tea-houses and retail shops and the workshops of countless craftsmen who furnish tools, utensils, vehicles, clothing, processed foodstuffs and many other things to the peasants. The larger cities have all the trappings of the commercial order—wharves, railway terminals, office buildings, factories, universities, department stores, and the rest.

The Occidental peasant landscape is quite distinct. Less dependent on flat irrigated lands, its cultivators make their fields on rolling slopes as well as in the valleys. The hillsides are often cleared and planted, but there are sometimes woodlots on the farms or communal forests near the villages. The countryside is dotted with gardens and orchards as well as fields, and cattle and other domestic animals are strongly in evidence. Again, a network of roads and canals, and an array of towns, cities, villages and isolated farmsteads mark the landscape.

There are many variations of this picture. On the shores of the Mediterranean, vineyards and orchards of chestnut, olive, fig and other trees are all up and down the rocky hillsides; and sometimes there are stone terraces to hold them there. As in the Orient, little fishing hamlets dot the coasts. The villages are compact, glaring, precariously hung on the slopes. There are irrigation ditches and reservoirs here and there.

In the desert regions from Morocco to Sinkiang cultivation is confined to the oases and the great river valleys. Groves of dates are a prominent feature in the Mediterranean part of this area. Squalid mud villages huddle on the riverbanks or amid the groves and gardens. Out on the desert margin there are camel trails leading to the next oasis or to the hills or coast.

Mountain country and the cooler coastlands show their own variations: widespread pastures, rocky little grainfields, now and again a village built of rock, treacherously steep and narrow roads, and daring bridges in the mountains. Everywhere there is a slightly different way of laying out the fields, of arranging the houses in the village, of using hillsides and bottom lands, forests and meadows, wet lands and dry lands.

Though there are variations, all around the middle of the world, from Shikoku and Bengal to Yemen, to Bavaria and Norway, some things are the same. The peasant landscape always comprehends an urban and a rural sector;[20] it always contains a net of well-used roads; it is largely open and cultivated; there are always places where raw resources are exploited, and places where finished articles are fabricated out of them, and these are always specialized activities in specialized locations.

The forms of society in which cultivation is the main activity of all the population command an effective technical order, and their members often attain considerable comfort, security and sophistication. The technical system that relates men to nature is generally one in which large common endeavors are exceptional. The essential economic unit, both of production and consumption, is still the family. The variety and quantity of consumer goods is limited to what the households individually can produce or occasionally acquire through trade at relatively great expense, and the decisions that regulate human effects in nature are taken mostly within the household.

Often the number of persons bound together in an interacting societal unit greater than the kinship unit is large, and the opportunities for contact with outsiders are numerous. Warfare is usually well developed in cultivating societies, and such refinements as slavery, cannibalism and headhunting are found among subsistence cultivators. There are also friendly ritual connections between neighboring or distant peoples, so that the occasions for encountering new ideas are frequent, and conditions for experimenting with change are often quite favorable.

The intermittent subsistence cultivators attain what at first sight appear to be rather high densities of population, with up to several hundred persons per square mile of plantings. Since, however, there are necessarily at least four or five times as much land usually left idle, the densities of shifting cultivators are actually much lower, and fifty to a hundred people per square mile is probably the highest concentration ever possible for these folk. Mostly their densities must be much lower. The figure of five persons per hectare (two per acre) at one time, equivalent to about 180 for each square mile of land actually used in a seven-cycle rotation of fourteen years, has been given for the East Indies.[21] Among the Zande of Central Africa, who are shifting cultivators, densities of from 13 to 43 per square mile are estimated for land in use.[22] In Yucatan a population of about 25 per square mile has been recorded.

Local variation in natural endowments, crops, and land use practices is so great that there is a great discrepancy among the density figures from one place to another even for the shifting cultivators. It is probably futile to attempt an estimate for the densities of sedentary horticulturists; and in the case of peasants, the introduction of the factor of exchange further complicates the picture. There are rural areas in such places as China, Java, and Bengal where the densities of people living on the land reach several thousands per square mile. These ratios represent an extreme, standing as they do for a situation in which the populations concerned are almost completely dependent upon the lands they farm and receive little from exchange.

In contrast, in fully commercial societies, urban densities of many thousand are often attained; and there is no necessary relation between the density of people in a particular place and its capacity to feed them from cultivation. Exchange establishes a different order of relations between populations and their habitats, and peasants and commercial folk attain a standard of living and a kind of security altogether unparalleled in other systems. Their peculiar situation and the reasons for it will be considered subsequently.

The impact of cultivators on the landscape is very great. The settled agricultural peoples clear large expanses of land permanently, substituting their fields for the former vegetation; and intermittent cultivators exert a constant pressure on vegetation as they clear their patches for brief periods, in some cases deflecting the development of the succeeding growth toward new forms. The soil is affected by the clean tillage of some farmers, the hillside clearing and the burning practiced by others. Soil impoverishment and accelerated erosion often follow in the wake of cultivation.

The various farming folk make large changes in other respects. Through felling timber for construction, cutting and collecting firewood, gathering vines for basketry and cordage, and systematically culling native plants for numerous uses, cultivating populations effect notable modifications of vegetation.[23] If they pasture animals, the pressure on vegetation is even more pronounced. Likewise they may reduce the population of game animals in their surroundings through continued trapping and hunting. Mineral resources in shallow situations are subject to heavy use. Wherever farmers occupy the land they remake it. Cultivation is still the vehicle of man's most widespread modification of the natural environment.

PASTORALISM

THE NOMADIC pastoral peoples have evolved a unique principle of organization. Their sustenance is largely derived from their animals, and their way of life consists in movements from place to place while pasturing the herds. The pastoral peoples have an obligate dependence on their animals, and their relative freedom from outside control rests on the fact that their connections with settled people have until recently been mostly facultative. The pastoral nomad reproduces the spatial patterns of the simple gatherers, though his techniques are vastly more complex. His economic universe is strongly influenced by the emphasis on social differentiation and kinship prevalent in nomad societies, and so exhibits reciprocal traits superimposed on a basically closed large-household form of economy.[24]

The pastoralists follow their herds of goats, sheep, bovine cattle, horses, camels, or reindeer, and control their migration over an extensive territory in search of the seasonally available plant food on which they depend. The compound symbiosis of animals and vegetation, and of men and animals, is expressed spatially in a round of regular treks between waterholes and pastures. During the course of the year the herd and its tenders move from lowland to highland and back, or from shore to inland regions. The herds multiply under the watch of man, and their masters take from them the animal stuffs and food they need.

The pastoral peoples load their beasts with the portable equipment of their camps. They sometimes possess very elaborate tents, utensils, containers, weapons, clothing, and the like, though their food supply is likely to be dominated by animal products from their herds.

Pastoral nomads are usually supplied with some plant food, either from small and poorly-tended plantations which they themselves sow, abandon and return to visit during their cycle of wanderings, or from settled lands of cultivation with which they maintain exchange relations. The pastoralists also depend upon settled folk for many of the artifacts they regularly use.

Because of their peculiar mode of life, the nomadic herders in the past have been able to exert great military power, out of all proportion to their numbers. They invaded and terrorized the civilized lands for three millenia. Dangerous and secure in a way of life whose economic-technical base, the animal, was completely mobile, the nomads could wage war wherever their herds could graze; they needed no supply lines. (Likewise the wanderers of the sea, secure in their ships.)

Today the pastoral nomads are in decline, under the influence of expanding exchange societies. In several countries they have been settled forcibly on the land. The opening of steppe lands to grain farming with machinery, and the extension of irrigated cultivation into many desert areas, as well as the growth of the territorial power of the sedentary states have worked against the independent and unruly nomadic way of life. Some of the Berbers of northwestern Africa are still true nomads, as are the Arab Bedouins from Morocco to Iraq, and some peoples of Turkic, Tibetan, Mongolic, and Iranian speech in Iran and Central Asia. There still are pastoralists, too, in the far north of the Soviet Union: such peoples as the Lapps, Samoyed, Tungus, and some of the Koriak and Chukchi. Many of the latter have been integrated into an exchange economy still preserving some essential features of their old way of life. Pastoral nomads did not occur in the New World before the coming of the whites; now, however, the Navaho shepherds are partially nomadic.

More common than the representatives of full nomadism are the many pastoralist groups who practice herding in conjunction with crop growing. In fact, some groups in Arabia have switched back and forth between nomadic herding, cultivation, and caravan trade and other services. *Transhumance* is a form of partial nomadism; in it people who possess settlements and fields drive animals during one season of the year from lowland to highland pastures. This practice is still quite common around the Mediterranean, where it is used with sheep, goats, and bovines. Such peoples as the Berbers of the mountains of Morocco and Algeria, and the mountain folk of Switzerland, the Caucasus and Anatolia, commonly follow this pattern. It is found elsewhere in countries settled by Europeans, notably in the western arid regions of the United States and in Australia.

Another form of pastoralism with settled sites occurs in Africa. Among the Nilotic peoples living in the swamps of the interior of the continent, fishing and cattle-raising are combined; and elsewhere in East Africa and the Sudan cattle raisers dwell in an intimate symbiosis with their animals and wander over the savannah lands from fixed villages or tribal centers. The same form of pastoralism appears in parts of Madagascar.

The pastoral tradition represents one form of mutualistic human symbiosis with domestic animals. A sedentary form of this symbiosis, in which the human partners tend domestic plants or manage a wild vegetation upon which the animals are fed, and in turn feed on the animals and their products, is characteristic of the more prosperous commercial societies. Meat and dairy products are the food of wealthy countries, whose ecological basis thus includes a complex set of symbiotic relationships, all mutualistic and obligate, between cultivators and plants, domestic animals and cultivated plants, food producers and non-producers, and consumers and domestic animals. The Scandinavian countries, Britain, the United States and Canada, Uruguay and Argentina, Belgium and the Netherlands, and Australia and New Zealand are the leading examples of countries whose commercial food-economy is built around the products of animals.

Pastoralism has been accused of bringing about very serious deterioration of vegetation and soil in areas where it has long been practiced. Around the Mediterranean, sheep and goats are blamed especially for the disappearance of plant cover and the washing away of soils. Herding in general may be an important factor in the development of grasslands.

The nomadic herders are in a way "capitalists," in that their investment in their animals is a form of accumulation, producing an increase of wealth akin to interest. They are, like modern commercial people, accustomed to wide contacts over great distances, and to highly organized political systems as one of the conditions of economic life; their traditionally expansionist policies, too, are suggestive of the commercial order. It is fitting now to look at the fully elaborated commercial economies, societies, and technical systems which manifest these and other distinctive properties in a remarkable way.

THE COMMERCIAL
ENVIRONMENT

THE ENVIRONMENT through which the nomad gatherers make their rounds remains, although its vegetation may be altered radically, almost as vast and empty as nature made it. In farming country, the cultivated fields and gardens display the handiwork of man, but the environments that they provide for crops remain ruled more by nature than by man. The city and the road are altogether artificial features, though, and commercial urban people live and work within environments that they impose on nature.

The wanderers live "off the land," garnering a livelihood from wild plants and animals; and farmers live "on the land," feeding themselves from their crops and livestock; but urban specialists live under highly artificial circumstances, lack the means of producing crops for themselves, and thus rely on rural populations to supply their food in exchange for other goods and services. We have observed that specialized commercial production of the kind associated with cities is possible only when, in addition to the food-producing symbiosis, there is a further symbiosis of exchange within the society that allows some of its members to engage in pursuits other than cultivation.

Large differences in artificial spatial arrangements are related to differences in economic forms. In subsistence societies, which have no appreciable exchange, all the various stages of production are carried out by the members of one very small household group in a small area. The complex of artificial features associated with production is "telescoped," and its component elements are little differentiated. Resource sites are few; routes of circulation are short and hardly improved; manufacture is carried on around the dwelling, and specialized services are few in number. Many parallel systems of production exist with little reciprocal effect, and the complexity and size of any one of them are limited by the small numbers of workers and the slight degree of specialization of the household group.

Societies in which much exchange is practiced display a different character. There, routes of transport link the many sites of resource exploitation, manufacture, and service; and along these routes are specialized installations for various kinds of commercial production. The artificial complex serves a large area, and tends to be connected with other like complexes. The productive system commands the labor and highly specialized skills of a large number of workers. The uses made of particular places, the equipment and installations devoted to particular tasks, and the working roles of individuals are all well differentiated and specialized.

A system organized around only the single symbiosis of food supply (subsistence) develops a multitude of unconnected, parallel economic units, each with its small complex of artificial productive features. The double symbiosis involving exchange in addition creates a single economic unit of wide scope, having one large and more or less unitary complex of highly specialized productive installations. The particular nature of this complex depends upon the degree of commercialization attained, i.e., the extent to which various commodities are subject to exchange.

CONSUMERS' AND PRODUCERS' ECONOMIES

AN *economy* regulates the circulation of goods and services, the physical means for which are embodied in the transport and communications system. The character of the economic organization therefore tends to be reflected in the material features of the man-made environment.

When exchange is absent, highly specialized production does not occur, and no commodities are made and moved to serve a general consumer class. The routes of circulation are, then, hardly developed, and practically no sites are set aside especially for manufacture or services (except those dedicated to ceremonial and political activity). There is no general economy among the social group, and there is no one system of artificial features deployed to serve an economic function for the whole society.

In a *peasant society,* one observes exchange relations between food producers and specialists in service and in manufacture. The cultivator grows food both for his own household and for an urban consumer population. In the city, specialized craftsmen devote themselves to the production of goods to be distributed throughout the society; services are performed for all by recognized specialists. One finds a general economic bond extending throughout the society, and an appropriate network of artificial sites and routes serving the economic life.

The economic system of a society of peasants and urban specialists typically rests upon an exchange of finished commodities among their specialized producers.[1] Each unit of production, or *firm*, acquires command of land or raw resources and processes commodities until they are ready for the consumer as final products. Exchange is a relation in this case among possessors of finished goods which can be traded for other finished goods. Although some of the commodities subject to exchange may serve productive purposes, as in the case of cultivating tools or cooking vessels, they are intended for permanent or terminal use in the form in which they are acquired, and not for incorporation into more evolved and complex products subject to further exchange. The handicraft shop is the characteristic manufacturing enterprise in such an economy. In it, all the necessary steps in the production of the finished article are accomplished, and often the services of retail trade are performed. The work is done by skilled craftsmen using traditional tools and simple machines. These artisans are closely integrated socially into one organized and fairly permanent group with a distinctive place in the society; often the many small handicraft enterprises are located side by side in a special quarter of the city. Raw materials are acquired by trade with the exploiters of natural resources or with cultivators of "industrial" crops, or are secured from properties controlled by the same enterprise that runs the shop. Typically, the tools and machines employed are designed, and are often even made, by the members of the shop group itself.

The situation of the peasant is closely analogous to that of the craftsman. He makes many of his tools and uses his own land or that of a proprietor. In an economy of peasants and craftsmen, therefore, exchange hardly intervenes in the productive process, but primarily affects finished commodities of consumption. An economy of this sort is a *consumers' economy.*

The *consumers' economy* represents an incompletely developed exchange economy. In it, land is seldom subject to frequent transfers of control. Land ownership and usufruct are usually hereditary rights closely linked with a stratified social order, and money or other mobile media of exchange cannot command them. Similarly, the equipment and installations used and occupied by productive enterprise are held by virtue of traditional claims. The actual processes of production, especially, are jealously kept secret by the guilds or other craftsmens' organization. The rights and the skills enabling a man to exercise a particular craft are difficult to acquire, and elaborate social arrangements rule the assignment of occupations. Neither land, nor capital, nor labor is subject to free exchange, and industrial processes are not subdivided into separate spatial stages carried on by different enterprises. There is almost no mobility of the factors of production. Limitations of skill rather than cost primarily govern the character and volume of commodities produced. The nature of the products offered in trade reflects the ability of single craft enterprises to command all the necessary techniques, materials, and equipment to carry through all steps in manufacture—all within a restrictive social milieu.

The limited scope for organization and control afforded by the consumer's economy restricts the availability of diverse and highly specialized producer's equipment and installations. These can be produced only at great expense and are not available through an exchange system under which only finished consumer goods circulate. Pre-modern textile and flour manufacturers built their own machines in the shop, and situated their wind- or water-mills in places where the enterprise could command adjacent inanimate power supplies. There were no true "public utilities" and almost no enterprises devoted exclusively to the supply of producers' goods. Few craftsmen worked entirely as producers of component parts for other enterprises' finished products.

The spatial order of the consumers' economy differs in many respects from that of subsistence economies. Consumers' economies possess concentrated urban settlements whose populations engage in manufacturing crafts and in services, and depend upon exchange with peasants for their food. A system of roads, sea routes, and sometimes canals, facilitates the movement of people and commodities. Natural resources are exploited to supply manufacturing units. Many service agencies, especially "public" ones, are concentrated in the urban settlements. The flow of production runs from the resource sites and farms over the roads to handicraft shops where the finished commodities are made; thence to the consumer through shops or the workshops themselves.

The types of installations made in these societies of peasants and craftsmen are, therefore, such as: *primary resource sites* at which raw materials for manufacture are produced: *public roads* and *canals* over which goods and people move; *workshops* in which the entire sequence of manufacture is centered; *cultivated lands* on which food for both their tillers and an urban populace is grown; *service centers* where goods are exchanged, public and private services offered, and social, religious, and administrative functions concentrated; and *settlements,* which vary from clusters of rustic huts to palaces, temples, and great cities. Residential buildings, civic and religious centers, monuments, and military fortifications are typically the most imposing artificial features of the landscape. Manufacturing enterprises are small and have no installations supplying them with large amounts of inanimate power. Their equipment is confined to numerous ingenious implements and utensils, machines built mostly from wood and driven by human or animal power, or at most by wind- and waterpower, and containers. Merchandising is carried on at the handicraft shops or small specialty stores; most retail agencies deal in a single kind of goods or services. Only in consumers' forms of *redistributive* exchange economies are great stores of diverse goods found. Pedestrians, pack animals, animal-drawn vehicles, and towed or wind-propelled watercraft travel the circulation routes. No special accommodations carry messages—with the exception of such things as lighthouses and signal beacons.

The manufacturing crafts still employ such materials as clay, wood, bone, hide, hair and fiber, though more complex products are developed from them, and the work is finer than where specialized crafts are absent. Metals are also in regular use, mainly for making small implements and utensils. Mineral fuels and wood are used in limited quantities for space-heating or in a few industries such as metallurgy. Water supply and sanitation are served by a network of conduits, reservoirs, and sewers, but little effort is made to protect the purity of water or to safeguard the population against dangerous wastes.

The same essential form of artificial environment develops wherever the consumers' economy occurs. It was characteristic of medieval Europe; the Islamic world at its height; millenial China; and, until recently, of Eastern Europe; it is even found, residually, in Latin America, and lives on here and there in the Old World. Although the peasants are still numerous, however, the old handicraft cities are rapidly disappearing, and are being replaced by modern industrial-urban complexes.

The consumers' economy, in which trade takes on great importance, requires certain social conditions in order to function.

Peaceful conditions must obtain to allow persons and goods to move with relative security. In some places, like Berber North Africa where there is a "market truce," or as in many Islamic countries where there is an annual period of moratorium on raids and warfare, the conditions suitable for trade are found only exceptionally. In other instances, trade flourishes within a circumscribed area where law and order are maintained by the power of a ruler. The value and volume of commodities entering trade respond to these conditions; and when risk is high, the profit sought is high, so that only goods of high value and low bulk are carried about for exchange. Military conquest, by extending favorable conditions of exchange, can promote prosperous trade, and the power of administrative agencies to guarantee the security of goods and persons within a state is of similar benefit to trade.

Bartering can be successful when just finished goods are offered, but it functions clumsily where a large and diverse assortment of products is involved. Some few accepted media of exchange, or one general medium, serve better; and where weights and measures, and especially the currency standard, are guaranteed by a central public agency, trade is favored.

Another requirement for exchange closely related to the above mentioned is the security of contractual relations. Trade is facilitated when a good or service can be exchanged not only against any other commodity at a given moment, but also by contract against future payment, services, or stocks of goods. Contract allows the exchange of future for present values. The contractual relationship also relies upon the guarantee of law and order, and upon some common medium for transacting exchanges. Contractual obligations are usually subject to enforcement by legal means.

Exchange under a consumers' economy demands, we see, not only physical means like the lines of communication, but also some degree of support and guarantee by public agencies. These must furnish at least a modicum of law and order, a monetary standard, and some legal protection of contractual relations. Although one or more of these conditions may be lacking at times, all of them and other like guarantees are ordinarily present in the consumers' economies. They are commonly provided by a comprehensive administrative and political unit, the state. Trade is, indeed, known in periods and places which lack the state organization, but the developed consumers' economy comprising symbiotic urban and rural sectors is closely dependent on the stability provided by organized political systems.

One of the distinctive features of *producers' economies* is that they are organized to effect a transfer of goods from one producer to another in unfinished form, as well as to govern transfers between producers and consumers. A firm now acquires goods, subjects them to partial preparation, and passes them on to other firms. Exchange enters into the regulation of the productive process itself, and there is a circulation not merely of finished goods, but of all the factors of production— land, labor, capital; and a single product is created in a number of different productive stages which take place successively in different locations, and are carried out by different firms. Production is serialized as well as specialized; and for each stage of production, the necessary materials and means are often assembled separately through exchange mechanisms.

The organization of production under a producers' economy differs from that under a consumers' economy. In the handicraft production associated with a consumers' economy, the technical basis of working organization is the complete product. Each enterprise commands all the tools, materials, and skills required to produce a given kind of article or a number of similar articles. Raw materials are turned, within the shop, into the final product. Leatherworkers in such enterprises may acquire raw hides which they clean, tan, dye, cut, fashion, and decorate to bring forth boots, garments, or saddles ready for use. They often sell them in the shop.

The factory enterprises of producers' economies are typically organized not to turn out a complete product ready for the consumer, but to perform only a part of the operations that produce it—the "job." A single factory may produce only the bolts that belong to a particular automobile assembly, or may only assemble pieces, already made elsewhere, into a toy. In many large enterprises, work is allocated among a number of different shops, each of which executes one or a few of the many operations that go to create the complex final product. An automobile factory, for instance, is a compound of many such shops, and in addition relies upon small independent plants to furnish certain of the parts it assembles.[2]

Production is broken down into a series of many separate jobs, and the whole process is spread out among many agencies over some distance. Different equipment and facilities are assembled at various points; all are connected by transport lines; and each is served by its own labor force. Skillful organization of the movement of materials through the proper sequence replaces skilled handiwork as the crucial element in production. Workers are readily trained, moved, discharged, or hired, and men take and leave jobs with little concern; no social traditions exclude all but a few groups from employment at a particular job, as is true with the crafts system. Equipment is not made on the spot, but purchased from special enterprises which design and produce it according to need. In some countries, the processes used in production are restricted to whatever enterprise can acquire legal rights over them, but eventually they become common property. Equipment and processes frequently change, personnel turns over rapidly, and even the nature of the product is constantly developing.

Since exchange makes available to producers services and goods that are created by other producers expressly for their use, a supply of specialized means of production, inanimate energy, component parts, and materials becomes accessible to any enterprise, regardless of its size. The large aggregate demand for productive goods and services supports the growth of a large producers' goods industry and of public utilities. A relatively high proportion of the factories and other manufacturing plants is devoted to the production (more technically, the conversion) of energy to operate other plants, to the production of materials—like pig-iron, sulfuric acid, and lumber—that are basic to other industries, and to the building of production equipment—like machine tools and chemical plants. A relatively small number of the manufacturing plants in operation under a producers' economy actually turn out only finished consumers' goods.

The spatial order associated with factory production reflects the great diversity of agencies concerned not only in production, but in the service of other production, and recently also in the service of urban populations employed in these activities. In the fully commercialized producers' economy, the unparalleled volume of exchange upon which production rests, the intricate division of tasks in manufacture, and the variety of services, all require an altogether unprecedented development of artificial facilities.

PRODUCTION CHAINS

LET US VISUALIZE the technical regime and spatial order associated with producers' economies with the help of some special but rather simple concepts. We return to an idea expressed earlier. If we define *production* as the efforts intervening between the discovery of a resource in nature and the ultimate consumption of the goods derived from it, we can lay out its spatial course. From resource site to residence, materials undergoing production are moved and halted, moved and modified, and moved again. This moving process of resource utilization confers upon materials three "utilities" of *place, time,* and *form.* The technical operations concerned take place in established sequences, and each of them is a phase of movement or rest through which the material passes in its progress toward completion. Fundamentally, technical production is movement. The productive apparatus of a modern industrial country is an infinitely complex but nearly unified mechanical system, so constructed that the intervention of man, exerting a controlling effect through his own bodily movements, manages it all.

The component operations of the manufacturing process are, according to the utilities of place, time and form, divisible into three types: *transportation, storage,* and *manufacturing proper.* The internal operations of a plant making radio apparatus show these three types, for example. The production line of the plant is laid out in such a way that successive stages in making the radio set are performed as the product moves slowly along, passing one task-position after another in the proper order. Along the workbenches sit employees assigned to add particular wires, plates, tubes, and so on; to tighten bolts; or to mount sub-assemblies. Before the workday begins and at frequent intervals as work progresses, a foreman or a parts man fills the bins alongside each worker with the appropriate parts. The worker fixes one such part to each of the pieces of apparatus coming through the line. A general stock-room holds the supply of parts, and receives new shipments from the receiving bay. From this stock-room, parts are distributed at intervals along the benches. Many of the parts and assemblies are received already fabricated from other plants, and are here only mounted in the final set.

The plant contains several different benches. Each builds a section of the whole radio set, and on the last stretch of its course, the production line carries the set past a bench of workers who tighten its mountings, inspect it, label it, and stack it for the packing room. Some of the workers coil wires and otherwise modify the form of materials, but most of them merely put together pre-fabricated parts. A radio factory's work is an example of *assembly*. This is one of the two chief operations in manufacture proper; the other is *processing*, in the widest sense.

If we observed a furniture factory, we would see that all along the production line the wood was undergoing modification. Pieces would be carved by power-planes, cut into lengths by saws, turned on lathes, drilled, bowed under steam and pressure, rasped and sanded; the joints would be morticed or drilled for bolts. Only after thorough mechanical deformation and reshaping would the parts be assembled, glued, and finished. Although a production line would probably be evident in the furniture factory (as against a handicraft shop), and the parts would move from storage through the line, the manufacturing operations would involve not merely assembly, but, preceding it, a whole series of steps in mechanical processing of the wooden parts. The assembly line phase of the furniture-making operation brings together the semi-fabricated parts made ready on other lines and in other shops within the factory.

Likewise, considerable difference occurs between the production and assembly lines of the mechanical industries and the production flows in chemical plants. In chemical manufacture, the mixing of materials is somewhat analogous to assembly; and heating, catalyzing, freezing, compressing, agitating, and the like resemble processing. The operations performed with chemical materials, however, are quite distinct despite these loose resemblances. Typically, the storage, movement, and modification of materials in a chemical plant take place in a continuous automatic or semi-automatic sequence in closed vessels and tanks. The material itself is mobile. At some points, however, some chemical products, notably such things as rubber, plastics, and other solid materials continue into a mechanical processing and assembly operation. Metallurgy stands out as a type midway between the chemical and the mechanical.

Our purpose here is not to discuss in detail the technology of manufactures,[3] but only to call attention to the essential operations of storage, movement, processing and assembly (or chemical mixing). The same general operations must, of course, be performed to create a given product whether the work is done in a craftsman's workshop or in a modern factory. The difference lies in the fact that in the factory production is laid out spatially in a smooth progression; this is not true in the workshop. Around the master spatial layout are organized the supply of materials, parts, and power, the stationing of equipment, the assignment of workers and supervisors, and even the accounting procedures of the enterprise. If the line is to operate as a smooth sequence, all equipment, personnel, parts, raw materials, and power must be marshalled in the right order. At each storage bin, shop, or station on the line, a task is performed that must succeed that of the stage before and make the developing product ready for the next step.

Auxiliary to the work on the line are administrative, supply, and maintenance service. A plant engineering department is concerned with layout and supervision. The business and accounting departments manage the whole operation financially and relate production to supply and demand conditions outside the plant. Personnel services engage and discharge workers, deal with the unions, and administer factory working conditions; and other agencies often operate cafeterias and social activities. Shipping and receiving and transportation arrangements are handled by a special section. A crew of maintenance men lubricate, adjust, and repair the machines, and often make parts and build new machines. A custodial staff tends to the cleaning and upkeep of buildings and grounds. The factory may have its own power plant, with a special staff. A great variety of such auxiliary activities can be found in many manufacturing plants.

The modern factory is "rationalized"; in effect, it is organized like a large machine.[4] If we examine the operation of a machine or chemical processing unit, we can discern the same group of fundamental operations. An unfinished metallic article is moved on a conveyor from a stack of pieces in a hopper in the machine; it is compressed, drilled, cut, or planed, and is moved along into another machine unit where it is welded or riveted to other parts.[5] A chemical reagent is pumped automatically from a storage tank into pipes feeding into a mixing trough, is mixed with other materials there, is stirred and heated, then is moved on to another tank for further combination. The schematic sequence here is analogous to that of the factory as a whole; both involve the same combination of storage, movement, processing, and assembly.

When the entire sequence of operations that contribute to the manufacture of a single complex product is considered, the scheme transcends not only any single machine, but any one plant, and the same way of visualizing manufacture can be applied over a series of different installations through which the product passes while in process. In the radio assembly plant, for instance, parts and sub-assemblies are received readymade, and fitted into the set. If we follow the parts back to their origin, we shall find that they have a long history of movement and change.

Consider the wires that are incorporated into the assembled radio set. They began as copper molecules bound in ore; perhaps they amounted to only a small percentage of its weight and bulk. The ore was dug or scooped from the earth, taken by short rail lines or trucks to a plant where it was crushed and perhaps floated and made into concentrates. After this it was moved to another plant, perhaps hundreds of miles away, by rail for smelting; it was put through a converter, perhaps elsewhere; then it was refined electrolytically. The metallic copper was shipped again to another firm where it was squeezed into wire. The wire was then sheathed with plastic, fabric, or rubber coatings, each with a comparably long history of its own. At last the prepared wire was stored in a warehouse, and thence shipped to the radio plant to be stored in the stockrooms. Many of the components of the finished radio have even more complicated histories than this.

Almost any industrial product in a producers' economy is passed through many different stages of storage, transport, and manufacture before being completed, and after production, is carried through an additional series of storage and transport stages until it reaches a consumer. The complex of artificial productive features is built to serve simultaneously a very large number of such different continuous operations. The progressive movement and modification of materials follow pathways selected from a great maze of routes of circulation, and pass through manufacturing sites situated thereon. Any completed product has come through a "chain" of productive operations deployed in space; the particular chain has been made up of segments of differing nature and length combined in accordance with the character of the product.[6] Since countless different products are being manufactured at the same time, infinite such production chains must be selected from the available complex. The spatial system as a whole thus consists of a basic network of sites and routes on which are laid, crisscross and running together, many different traffic patterns. The commercial landscape is dominated by densely settled urban points, connected by traffic routes over which move shipments in all directions.

The patterns selected from the developed network of sites and routes are very unlike for production and consumption, respectively. Production movements have a linear form. We may describe the gradual evolution and assembly of the final product as the outcome of a series of additions of material and energy made to any component material as it is moved from the resource site to the consumer's home. The line of production receives branches where each addition of materials or parts is made, or where power is applied. These branches represent subsidiary lines of production from which components are derived, including in themselves the operations of transport, storage, and manufacture. If we were to display the diagram of production of the radio set, we should find along the line of whatever component we chose as central—say the copper wire— a set of different branches to represent each addition: the aluminum mounting-plates, the tubes, the cabinet, the bolts, the switches, and so on. On each of these branches we should see many points at which lesser branches would strike off. At each junction of a branch with the line, and at all junctions along the lesser branches, we should find a plant of some kind, with appropriate equipment, materials, power supply, labor, and auxiliary services. The ramifications of the diagram would be almost without end, and the number of plants and resource sites involved would be tremendous. The diagram for any very complex product would soon involve a large part of the whole national and international economy and productive system.

The linear diagram of production thus develops into a multipinnate scheme, often reaching great complexity. Thousands of such production lines, blending and separating, coexist within a single industrial country. Here and there a particular kind of bolt is incorporated both into radios and into television sets; at this point two lines are linked by branches meeting. A line representing the mining, refining, and chemical alteration of mineral pigments meets and fuses with the line of vegetable oil extraction, purification, and blending, and together they become a diagram of paint production; the oils have also, in part, been destined for use in foodstuffs, and so the line showing their manufacturing fate must be split off in two directions.

Consumption, on the other hand, follows very different spatial patterns. Let us consider the case of consumption—not only the act of use itself, but also the services that make goods available to consumers, including wholesaling, warehousing, distribution of commodities, and retailing. All the paths of movement converge upon a consumer household. A number of different products are used in the household; thus a number of different lines run into it. We depict consumption, therefore, by a radial diagram. A relatively small number of retail outlets provides the consumer with what he uses. If we were to represent each of the hundreds or thousands of different products consumed by a separate line, the lines would fall into a few fascicles at the retail store; behind it, there would be only a few connecting lines between store and wholesale warehouses; the warehouses would be fed by lines of supply from factories, food-processing plants, and other producers.

Production brings materials together, and is represented by converging branch lines in our diagrams. Consumption requires the dissemination of goods and services among people, and so is represented by lines diverging from producing agencies and converging at one point on each consumption household. A different diagram for consumption could theoretically be constructed for every single household.

If the many slightly different individual patterns in any one community are grouped together, however, another pattern emerges that represents the intermediate stages of distribution, and that generalizes the picture of commodity flow at the level of relations among different settlements. A "hierarchy" of places serving different but connected stages of the distribution function is displayed.[7] This arrangement is possible because certain settlements, usually very large ones, contain the specialty warehouses; somewhat lesser centers contain warehouses with mixed stock; still smaller places contain only retail stores. We find the same relations among the respective settlements in regard to numerous different branches of merchandise supply and services; therefore, the principle of territorial hierarchy can be generalized.

The traffic concerned both in production and in the service of consumption—for movement is the essence of both—flows through a single net of sites and routes that describe the figures of the ramifying linear production chain or the converging lines of the consumption rosette. The same circulation routes serve both sorts of activity, and the same settlements are the scenes of production and of consumption simultaneously. Of all the artificial features of environment, therefore, we recognize that agglomerated settlements and routes of circulation stand out as peculiarly important in commercial countries.

The urban place, from the standpoint of manufacturing, is a node on the production line at which some job is performed on a given product; the line of production for any one product may run through many cities. From the standpoint of consumption, the urban concentration is a service center, hierarchically ranked according to the functions performed in it, and is also the site of residence of a population of consumers—the "end of the line" from natural resources. A manufacturing plant itself is to some extent a unit of consumption; it requires not only raw materials and semi-finished products, but also many other goods and services in order to operate. Labor is clearly one of these needs. The operation of the plant is contingent also on certain public services, and, as we have noticed, a host of professional and private services may be auxiliary to the work on the production line itself. The plant usually depends upon public utilities to deliver to it water, gas, and sometimes power, and to dispose of its wastes. It relies upon a retail trade center and upon banking, legal, medical, and other such services in its community. Its personnel, at all levels, require a vast number of public, semi-public, and private services. In the industrial countries where producers' economies prevail, therefore, the role of settlements as service centers, and the functions of circulation, are of particular interest and importance.

CIRCULATION

MODERN INDUSTRIAL PRODUCTION requires the movement, not only of the materials in process, but also of the people, equipment, auxiliary materials, information, and energy involved in its operation. The traffic necessary to the function of a manufacturing system includes much besides raw materials and un-

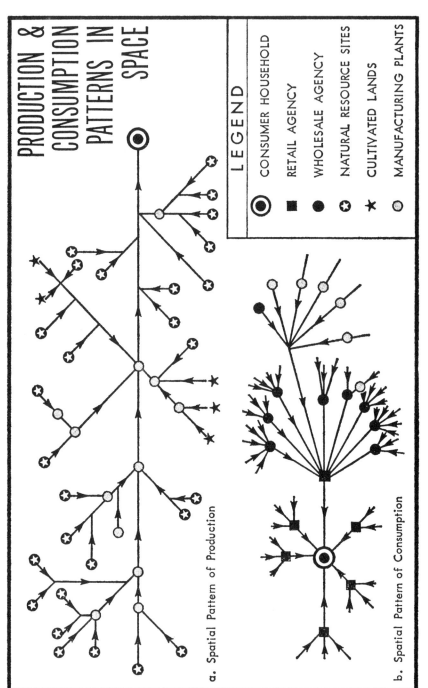

PRODUCTION & CONSUMPTION PATTERNS IN SPACE

LEGEND

◉	CONSUMER HOUSEHOLD
■	RETAIL AGENCY
●	WHOLESALE AGENCY
✪	NATURAL RESOURCE SITES
★	CULTIVATED LANDS
◍	MANUFACTURING PLANTS

a. Spatial Pattern of Production

b. Spatial Pattern of Consumption

Figure 7

finished goods. All of this diverse traffic will be described by the general term, *circulation*.[8] Following the French usage of the word, we shall let circulation mean the movement not only of goods, but also of people, raw materials, messages, and money.

Whereas sedentary cultivators settle immediately upon the resource of the soil and exploit it in place, and the nomadic gatherers circulate in their wanderings among resource sites, the people of an urban industrial producers' economy tend to work in stationary sites and to cause all the necessary resources and manufactured goods and even some services to circulate among them. A technical order based on this kind of circulation represents an attempt to equalize the availability of all means of production over space.

The facilities for circulation were discussed in Chapter 7. They fall into three categories: *lines for the transmission of messages, routes of transport,* and *utilities.* Of the three, only transportation routes are found in any abundance associated with consumers' exchange systems. The transport lines of the fully urban industrial system, however, provide not only routes for private travel, but a regular service as carriers of large volumes of freight and persons. The highways carry buses and trucks offering public service; and railroads, barge lines, steamship lines, and airlines conduct commercial operations. These carriers furnish almost all of the transport service for the whole productive system. The business of transportation is a specialized, separate branch of commercial activity.

Each form of transport line displays its own peculiar physical and institutional attributes. Motor transport service, which is at present highly developed mainly in the United States, Canada, and Western Europe, depends almost entirely on private carrier lines, but these in turn operate over public roads. The building and upkeep of roads and bridges is a public charge supported by taxation. A further peculiarity of motor transport is the absence of concentrated single terminals for the movement of cargoes. The automotive transport agencies can serve any spot accessible by road, which means that freight may be picked up or delivered almost anywhere. The capacity per vehicle is relatively small, so motor service is better suited

to smaller and more varied cargoes than to large volumes origi-
nating always at the same point. The automotive carriers rank
among the more rapid means of transport both of goods and
persons.

Though this is no place for a thorough discussion of transport, we may well take note of the properties of the other main
carrier systems. The railroad requires a high initial investment,
and its operation is not nearly so flexible as the motor carrier's.
Until quite recently, most railways were built by private enterprise. Great expense is sometimes involved in laying out road-
beds at proper grade, in bridging streams and canyons, and in
traversing unstable ground; the requirements are stricter in
these cases for railroads than for highways. Railroads are committed to fixed routes and to concentrated, permanent terminals;
motor traffic is not. Railroads operate best where large volumes
of bulk freight are constantly available at one point.

Water carriers need maintain only terminal facilities, and
often these are provided by public agencies. Also publicly provided are breakwaters, channel-deepening, navigational markers
and signals, pilot service, and other services. The route followed
is laid out over open water. Both inland and ocean water transport is suited to carriage of large bulk cargoes at low unit cost
and over long distances. They can, of course, serve only points
on the water bodies concerned. Ocean carriers, like railroads, are
privately operated in some countries; in others, they are very
heavily subsidized by public funds; and elsewhere, state-owned.

Airlines, again, have no routes to maintain, but must use a
few concentrated terminals. Air freight is costly, and suitable
only for high-value or urgent cargoes. Airlines are also either
state-owned, subsidized, or entirely private, depending on the
country.

Circulation, in a producers' economy, is thus dependent upon
a few kinds of transport lines serving public needs for the carriage of persons and cargoes.

A second kind of facility of circulation, which is especially
important under the producers' economy, is the "public utility."
Let us restrict the term here to mean single substances or single

forms of energy transported en masse and continuously from natural sources to both consumers and producers, or, in the case of wastes, away from their producers. Public utilities are served by a permanent network of conduits of one kind or another. The only utility regularly associated with consumers' economies is public water supply for rural and urban uses; under producers' economies, we can list in addition waste disposal—sewage and garbage removal—and the supply of both fuels and electric power to consumers and producers.

As a city is served by roads and usually by railroads, airlines, and water transport lines, it is also provided with a system of reservoirs, tanks, and pipes through which water flows, coming from some more or less distant collecting points. Water for domestic use and for industry is essential to a city, and artificial means of supply are considered necessary in a settlement of any size. The flow of water after use is a vehicle for the removal of wastes; thus a further maze of pipes leads into sewers, and to treatment plants or disposal areas.

Like water, liquid petroleum products may be carried into the city in pipes and stored in tanks. The oil is sometimes brought overland by pipe, with frequent pumping stations pushing it along, all the way from the fields to the consumers; sometimes it is carried part of the distance by railway or by ship. Natural and artificial cooking and industrial gas is also stored in tanks and distributed by pipe to consumers. Gas is sometimes brought from natural-gas fields, or is sometimes manufactured from coal. (We shall not count coal, wood, and similar fuels as public utility items, however.)

Electric power is the third major public utility category. A complex network of lines and stations converts energy into electric form and carries and regulates its flow to consumers. In some places hydroelectric power is most important, in others, power made in thermal plants burning oil or coal, and in yet other places, peat. Electric power is basic to modern industry and advanced consumer standards. This energy is usable in any quanitity and is readily circulated. For these reasons, it lends itself to the flexible operation of industrial equipment at any scale as well as to the powering of small household appliances. A large portion of all industrial machines and consumers' equipment in use today is electrically operated.

In addition to the transportation lines and the public utilities, the communications media that carry messages should be counted as facilities of circulation. The association of literacy with cities is ancient. Only in very recent times have the communications media proliferated. The radio, telephone, telegraph, and television have grown up in conjunction with the other facilities of circulation (especially electric power) and with the complex means of production of the twentieth century. Specialized and costly installations are required for them, as for utilities and carriers.

The foregoing hasty sketch suggests the nature of the facilities involved in circulation, and the sort of traffic they carry. It should be remarked that the arrangement of circulation within an urban settlement is rather different from that without. In the cities there are routes leading to the residences of consumers, to service installations, and to manufacturing plants. The lines of distribution of traffic along the way toward the consumer become more and more ramified; they fan out from the central point at which they enter the settlement, and branch repeatedly, in a way analogous to the spatial order previously described for consumption of goods.

Thus, for cities in the United States, the U.S.S.R., most of Europe, Australia, New Zealand, and Canada, and for most of the larger urban settlements elsewhere, we may describe a generally similar circulation complex as follows. Pedestrian and animal movement, and most vehicular traffic are served by a grid of streets, mostly paved, which subdivide the city into many small blocks. Some of the streets are wide, others very narrow; some serve rapid traffic; others permit only a slow stream of movement. A single system of underground pipes provides water to some or all residential districts and to industries; in most cities private wells still provide water too. Another underground pipeline system carries away the sewage of the settlement, and usually dumps it into a nearby water body. A grid of electric transmission and distribution lines, partly overhead and partly underground, serves homes, shopping districts, and factories with power; some large manufacturing plants produce their own power. Another network of wires carries telephone communication, and another, telegraphic. Radio and television instruments pick up emissions from local or distant stations. Natural gas is piped in, or a local works makes gas from coal; this is then distributed to households and firms. What circulates over these facilities, of course, depends upon certain other arrangements that will be discussed presently.

Now, if we compare the rural situation with the urban one just described, we find that in contrast to the much-ramified networks of the city, the cross-country facilities of circulation are few but of large scale. We usually find a few railroad lines, and often canals and highways. Lanes of air traffic pass overhead. Large pipelines carry petroleum or gas. High-tension cables conduct electric power from its sources, and telephone or telegraph lines, sparsely strung between the cities, carry messages. Here and there an irrigation canal or ditch may appear. The visible routes of circulation are relatively few, but run for very long distances and are capable of carrying a large volume of traffic.

It is notable that in the commercial rather than the peasant countryside, the farmsteads are often linked to the great lines of communication that pass near them. The agricultural enterprises are served, much as are manufacturing ones, by the highly developed circulation system, and they are closely connected with the "greater world" of the cities.

We must consider now the influences that govern circulation by way of these facilities. We may assume that in the producers' economy, as in the consumers', certain guarantees are required in order that the productive system may flourish. Among these guarantees we may list again the maintenance of law and order, a common monetary standard, and the stability of contractual relations. These are provided by services of the state.

The complex circulation associated with industrial producers' economies demands many further guarantees, which are mostly provided by various service centers. We have noted the need for law and order. In a modern commercial, urban country there is customarily a sizeable army to defend the state against foreign enemies, or acquire new territories and privileges. The army and other institutions also may be instrumental in repressing civil disorder. In addition, national and local police agencies regulate, if not suppress, crime. Ordinarily the police provide sufficient protection of property to foster commercial activity.

The institution of property itself must be mentioned as another guarantee. In Soviet society, property claims are almost all vested in the state, in the name of the people; this is apparently a satisfactory way of regulating the use of property. In most other instances, private property is maintained. This is only one of a great number of institutional forms forming the "climate" of economic life. It is administered, arbitrated, and adjusted through the legal and legislative structure. The existence of such an explicit institutional system, and of public service agencies to expound it, may well be indispensable for the function of a complex modern industrial economy.

Among the semi-public, professional, and private services, those having to do with finance, education, research, public health, engineering, and merchandising are obviously important influences on the circulation pattern. It is unlikely that an intense interchange of goods, claims, population, and ideas could go on without common denominators of value and means of transferring credit; without basic grounds, in education, for mutual intelligibility; without constant attempts, through the various branches of pure and applied research, to correct existing deficiencies of the system and to improve it; or without adequate provision for disposal of goods and services among consumers. The last item—merchandising and its associated services—can be perhaps the most crucial of all, and the one most effective in regulating all circulation; but such can be the case only in market economies, not in redistributive ones (e.g., the U.S.S.R.'s) where consumption demand need not influence production.

What is it, then, that circulates (under the influence of the service agencies) over the routes of circulation? First, the materials undergoing production pass along transportation lines and through the factories. The finished manufactured products then move out to consumers. Further, agricultural products move toward consumers through the distributional system—as do power, fuels, water, and other utility items. An invisible movement in the opposite direction carries monetary balances. Cash or credit changes hands as materials move and turns up as debit or credit entries on the books of the enterprises concerned; later actual transfers of deposits, banknotes, or gold may occur— after the simplifying procedure of bank clearance. Messages move on the routes of circulation in both directions; orders for purchase, invoices, bills of lading, statements of account; queries and instructions and reports and requests concerning commercial matters. A flood of paper and words issues from each administrative agency as well. Private letters and telephone messages, books, magazines, and newspapers also circulate from one place to another. People, furthermore, rush or amble about, and ride or fly along the routes. There is, in other words, a constant movement of human beings, vehicles, aircraft, and vessels; a pulse of power and petroleum and gas; a stream of fresh water and an ebb of wastes; a flow of raw and finished materials; a brisk exchange of money; a ceaseless tide of words, spoken or written or grimaced on television. Without this lively circulation, interlaced and intricate, the whole complex commercial order probably could not survive for a minute.

In the urban centers, with their denser network of communication lines, the circulation is that much the more intense. Almost everything that moves in this artificial world, indeed, passes through the cities. As in consumers' economies settlements constitute a hierarchy of service centers connected with the functions of circulation. The larger railroad yards are situated near big centers, and most of the mainliner trains pass through them; the telephone trunk lines run between metropolitan centers; the electric networks are controlled from a few centralized nervecenters; finance is ruled by a national or a nationwide reserve bank and by commodity and security markets in a few places. Control of the whole circulation pattern is centralized in a limited number of centers, and is exercised through subsidiary centers down the hierarchical chain of command. The circulation is carried on a network of routes which are usually coterminous with a national state. The whole system is governed by a few service centers, mostly urban, within that state. The countryside is intimately bound into the same system unless a peasant population continues to conserve its local roots and preferences.

THE COMMERCIAL COUNTRYSIDE

ANOTHER DISTINCTIVE FEATURE of producers' economies is that the land and its resources are bought and sold as readily as any commodity. Agriculture functions to produce crops and animals entirely for sale, not for use by the rural population. Natural resources are sought and developed wherever possible in order to meet the demands of industrial production. The fisheries, forests, farms, and mines feed raw materials into circulation and specialized production where they are converted into final products by many different machines, operated by inanimate power under the guidance of skilled workers. The contribution to production of "land," which represents the output of cultivated fields and resource sites, is adjusted to the capacities of capital and working force to process raw materials, and of consumers to absorb the finished products. The rate of raw material production is adjusted accordingly by pricing mechanisms or by systematic plan.

The investment in equipment and installations, the application of labor, the use of auxiliary materials and inanimate power, and the disposition of the product all are weighed in relation to return on the investments made. The farmer invests in mechanized equipment, irrigation, improved seed, fertilizer, fencing, barns, silos, and other capital goods to increase his production. He hires seasonal labor. He buys and fattens animals on feeds that he produces or purchases. He has an opportunity to use specialized goods, such as farm machines and soil supplements; to employ the specialized services of veterinaries, poultry hatcheries, credit organizations, producers' cooperatives, and so on; and to apply such specialized management procedures as erosion control, afforestation, stock-breeding, and cover cropping. The agricultural enterprise, and the exploitation of forest tracts, mineral deposits, or fishing banks, can be treated as "rationalized" industrial ventures in which the operator calculates his best advantage and invests accordingly in technical means, materials, and labor. This does not imply, of course, that such an approach is invariably taken. Guess and habit are commonly guides to action in farming and resource exploitation, and, for that matter, in manufacturing and services. "Rationalized" production involves the bringing together of special means to achieve a given end, but it does not ensure that the selection or use of these means will be wise or "rational."

The exploitation of natural resources and the cultivation of the land are both highly selective. Although the earth is full of aluminum, iron, manganese, and many other elements, the exploitation of minerals occurs at only a few sites where concentrations of particular compounds are extensive enough to yield a high content of the metals in a form suitable for processing. Most mineral deposits are left unused. Similarly, timber is cut commercially in a relatively few small spots at any one moment, and most forested country is never exploited because its stands are too sparse, too small, too mixed, or too remote. The extent of land actually cultivated, too, is greatly exceeded by territory left unused, held in fallow, or employed only for grazing animals; only a small portion of the soil can be farmed, and not all of that is used at once. Again, only a minute fraction of the potential energy in moving waters is ever harnessed; the size or situation of most streams precludes the economical utilization of their energy.

In a peasant economy, the cultivator strives to grow what his household will consume, and to have enough besides to pay his debts and taxes and to trade for necessary consumer goods. The peasant must till the land that is traditionally his to work, and grow the crops demanded by the customary diet and crafts. He does not often save enough to invest extensively in improvements and equipment, or to purchase much additional land. The installations on a peasant farm, and the fertility of its fields, are usually the fruit of generations of labor, in which local materials and homemade tools have been used almost exclusively. The peasant can seldom choose the land he farms, the crops he grows, or even the tools and facilities he uses.

The commercial farmer, on the other hand, armed with savings and credit, selects a crop to cultivate according to the prospects of the market and his own skills and preferences. He acquires suitable land, if he does not possess it, through lease or purchase, and assembles the necessary equipment and supplies. The outcome of the complicated interplay of land and climate, skills and management, and equipment and improvements can be calculated to some extent, and on this basis there is a tendency toward specialization of crop areas. Consideration of comparative advantage comes into play, causing the production of particular crops to become localized, ideally, within the area where the best combination of market and production factors can be achieved with least investment. The commercial countryside, therefore, is divided into relatively specialized agricultural regions, in each of which a few particular combinations of crops predominate. The location and total extent of a given crop region respond to specific economic considerations.

Regional specialization of agriculture occurs to a much lesser extent in peasant lands, where food crops for the rural population are usually the first consideration. Specialization is realized to a considerable degree, however, among the peasants of the Soviet Union, and the "socialist" countries, where government planners assign crop quotas and make local food supply secondary. Under a market economy, specialization of crop regions is affected by political factors, so that comparative advantage applies only within national boundaries and between very dissimilar countries. A classic example is the artificially promoted development of sugar beet production in extra-tropical areas, despite the advantages of tropical cane production; another well-known instance is the furtherance of butter production through the imposition of high taxes on oleomargarine. Tariffs, import quotas, taxes, and subsidies protect relatively uneconomical agricultural activities.

The State of California offers an outstanding example of great local crop specialization under a market economy, which is related to differences of climate, soil, and relief, as well as to the position of circulation routes, the sites of the canneries, packing sheds, and other installations for processing crops, the residential and crop preferences of immigrant groups, the labor supply, and other factors. In the Central Valley and the Salinas Valley, wheat and barley are important crops for food and fodder; rice is grown extensively on irrigated lands on the lower Sacramento River, and sorghum and millets on the upper Sacramento. The south is noted for citrus crops; lemons and grapefruit are grown commercially as far north as the Sierra Madre, and oranges are also found in the Sierra Nevada foothills. Avocados are raised around San Diego, dates at Indio, almonds in the upper Salinas Valley and the northern Sacramento Valley. Pears, peaches, apricots, and prunes are grown in the counties around San Francisco Bay and in the San Joaquin Valley; walnuts, at the feet of the Mount Hamilton and Solano ranges; apples, in the Pajaro alley, in Sonoma County, and the Mother Lode country; cherries, in the Santa Clara Valley; olives, in Tehama County; figs, at Fresno. Salinas exports lettuce; Stockton, asparagus; Castroville and San Luis Obispo, artichokes; Santa Clara, strawberries; Kern County, potatoes; Modesto, melons; Santa Maria, peas; the Imperial Valley, carrots, squash, onions, watermelons, and many other products. Hillside vineyards in Sonoma, Napa, Alameda, and Santa Clara Counties produce grapes suitable for making fine dry wines; grapes for sweet wines and for the table come from the rich irrigated lands of the San Joaquin, and from the Los Angeles Plain. Cattle and sheep graze in the southeastern deserts and in the mountains, and feed on alfalfa from irrigated plots. There are dairy ranches near the cities and up and down the western San Joaquin Valley.[9]

Not many states and countries are so diversified in their agriculture as California, but the same condition of regional specialization is found to some degree wherever market relations apply. There is a similar specialization in the exploitation of natural resources generally. Thus, commercial timber cutting takes place in the forests of the Pacific Northwest of the United States; in the redwood belt of the north coast of California; in the Sierra Nevada and Cascades; and in the pine woods of the South. Commercial fishing is based mainly on very large and dependable populations of such single species as the halibut, mackerel, cod, salmon, and smelt, which are exploited by special fleets. Most of the catch is taken at a few choice fishing grounds, and fishing for varied catches in less rich waters is much less significant in a market country. Copper is another resource occurring in widely scattered deposits, of which only a few of the richer ones are usually exploited. Many different ores of copper could be smelted, but only a few are commercially workable. Even so, over a third of the states of the United States have been producing copper in recent decades, though in a relatively few sites. Montana, Utah, and Arizona are the only large producers.

In the exploitation of natural resources, as in agriculture, the producers' economy brings a specialization of production in the most favored sites and regions, and concomitantly, favors the practical disregard of smaller, poorer, less accessible resources or inferior lands. This tendency is precisely opposite to what goes on with regard to the facilities of circulation, manufacture, and consumption. The effect of circulation is to carry more of fewer things from each of a smaller number of more favored regions, and to spread them and their final products nearly uniformly everywhere. Though each part of the United States is known for distinctive agricultural products and raw materials, consumption patterns are remarkably similar throughout the country. Southern Florida is noted for sponges, gamefish, tropical fruits, and cigars; western Washington for salmon, lumber, berries, and dairy products. Eastern Virginia produces sweet potatoes, hams, and peanuts; the north coast of California redwood lumber, hops, apples and peas. But from Tampa to Tacoma, and from Cape Hatteras to Cape Mendocino, the department stores, filling stations, drugstores, sport shops, and "supermarkets" are almost alike. The restaurants offer the same fare; everyone smokes the same cigarettes, drinks the same soft drinks, and whistles the same tunes. The consumers are homogenized.

The uniformity of everything from television commercials

to ladies' underwear and salad dressings over an area of three million American square miles (plus Hawaii and Alaska) is a result of the gigantic scale of manufacture, the use of standardized methods and equipment and materials, the growing centralization of merchandising operations, and the intensity of circulation within the country.

Mass production and the mass market make heavy demands upon raw materials. Another characteristic of agricultural production and resource exploitation under the producers' economy, therefore, is the large volume of output of few and specialized enterprises. The concentration of exploitation upon choice forests, rich mineral deposits, great schools of fish, and so on, and the selection of the best-suited growing sites for particular crops, account for the large volume of production, in part because they promote a high return for each unit of investment. Another powerful influence is the application of industrial production methods and "economizing" techniques to the allocation of production factors in primary production. Efficiency of operation is enhanced through such measures as intensive research, the provision of large sums of financial capital for investment, the development of sources of cheap electric power, the invention of numerous machines for special uses, the maintenance of a high level of education and training among the working population, and the construction of abundant facilities for circulation. Thanks to these and other measures, the productivity of workers, the unit output of plant, the rate of extraction, and the yield of land have risen, in the United States, Japan, northwestern Europe, Canada, Australia and New Zealand, and a few other countries, to unparalleled levels. In some other countries, like the Soviet Union, the fully commercialized industrial sector, including the exploitation of natural resources, has risen at equal or even greater rates, but agricultural production has not grown correspondingly. The still incomplete absorption of the peasantry into the commercial system, despite the most strenuous and brutal efforts of the state, may explain the lag.[10]

The Soviet case is an example of incomplete development, so far, of the producers' economy. Investment in the facilities

of circulation, natural resource exploitation, and heavy manufacturing plants has been remarkable over the last thirty or
forty years, but the manufacturing industries serving consumers,
and the services, have, like agriculture, been slow to develop.

No commercial country produces within its own borders all
the raw materials it uses. The localized rich mineral deposits
and timber stands, and the favored specialized crop regions
are comparatively few, and they are scattered all over the world.
Regional specialization inevitably exists on an international
scale as well as within countries. An example is the division
of crops between the tropics, the "Mediterranean" areas, and
the higher latitudes, as well as between different altitude zones
of the tropics. From the wet tropical lowlands are exported
bananas, cacao, rice, balsa, abaca, pepper, jute, copra, vanilla,
and rubber, for instance; the drier lowlands furnish hardwoods,
gums, sugar, cotton, pineapples, and many spices. Tea and
coffee are specialties of tropical highlands and the cooler lowlands. The mild dry-summer zones of "Mediterranean" climate
export citrus, other fruits, vegetables, and grains. In higher latitudes, potatoes, grains, fodder, and industrial crops are especially grown. As a result of circumstance, some agricultural
products are almost entirely associated with one country; the
fiber crops, abaca in the Philippines and jute in Bengal, are
examples. Various kinds of lumber are even more local in origin,
being cut from completely differentiated native vegetations.
Teak comes entirely from Burma and neighboring countries, true
mahogany and Spanish cedar from tropical America, redwood
from California, ebony from Africa and southern Asia.

Different minerals are likewise pinpointed. Nickel is practically all mined in eastern Canada, the Russo-Finnish border
regions, north Burma, and New Caledonia. Virtually all of the
world's tin comes from Bolivia, Southeast Asia, and Central
Africa. Sizable phosphate deposits are known only in the southern United States, northwestern Africa, the Kola peninsula, and
a few Pacific islands. The requirements for given metals are
highly specific in the metallurgical industries because of the
great differentiation of the many uses to which particular metals
are put. Each mechanical task makes exacting demands for

materials of particular capabilities and tolerances. Similarly, the demands of chemical industries for materials are highly particular. The mineral products in demand by agriculture are mostly soil supplements; they are varied, but only a few, like phosphates and potash, are required in large amounts. Industrial requirements for products of agriculture (and gathering)— like oil, solvents, pigments, waxes, alkaloids, starches, gums, fibers, and animal products—are also rather precisely fixed by technical practices. The specificity of demand for countless industrial materials calls forth a worldwide trade in specialized products, then, and leads to regional differentiation of primary production all over the earth. Whereas primary production, because of its dependence on natural conditions, is thus distributed among many countries, the activities of processing and finishing are concentrated in the manufacturing plants of a few cities, mostly in the minority of countries where capital is abundantly available.

Since the industrial countries depend for raw materials upon the resource sites and cultivated lands both within and without their own frontiers, there is a tendency toward complementary specialization between industrial, highly commercial countries like Great Britain and France, and less commercialized raw-material suppliers like their former colonies. The same relation may obtain between the more and the less developed regions within a single country. On the other hand, the respective partners may all be politically independent. In any case, the industrialized metropolitan nation or district establishes *outposts* in the raw material area which are islands of producers' economy and of high investment amid much less commercial surroundings.

The outpost represented by plantation agriculture produces almost all of the tropical specialty crops. Many important mineral commodities of world commerce, too, and some kinds of lumber, come from similar colonial outposts. Plantations are usually located on or near good transport routes, and embody large investments; mines and forest enterprises, and especially the transport lines that serve them, also represent great investment. Not all of these outpost enterprises are, or remain, under the control of metropolitan investors. In Malaya, for example, both rubber and tin are produced in large part by independent Chinese operators. Most of the cacao of Ghana and the coffee of Costa Rica is produced by small farmers. In some places shifting cultivators who employ slash-and-burn methods produce crops like pepper, or tree-crops for market. Pastoral nomads raise sheep in part for sale to cities in the Middle East. Even true collectors and gatherers are occasionally employed to exploit the forest. In this way the Aeta of the Philippines are hired to hunt game; the Central African Pygmies, to kill elephants for ivory; and the Amazonian Indians, to collect rubber, carnauba nuts, and other products. The plantation and other outposts of the commercial world bring all sorts of groups into relations with the outside.

Extractive enterprises of the producers' economy introduce or intensify commercial relations wherever they occur. They offer opportunity for local folk to earn wages and to spend or even accumulate cash, perhaps for the first time. They bring trade outlets for manufactured goods and the lure of foreign luxuries. Because laborers from foreign areas are often introduced to work on plantations or in mines, and because they are usually fed imported foodstuffs and are not allotted land, they form a new commercial element which becomes incorporated into the population of the receiving country. Along with this laboring personnel, exotic traders appear; or some of the imported workers establish themselves as merchants. Thus, we find the Chinese as traders and city folk in Malaya, Southeast Asia, the Philippines, and the Caribbean area; Lebanese and Syrians, in West Africa and Latin America; Indians and Arabs, in East Africa; and Indians, in Fiji, Trinidad, and Guiana. Such colonies of traders have existed no doubt since trade began.

Since the commercial centers of those countries mainly producing raw materials are directly linked to the producers' economy of the world market, they tend to be cities partly of the "Western" type. In them are manufacturing plants and services and circulation of the same sorts familiar in the metropolitan countries. Often these cities are sharply divided into "European" or "Western" and "native" sectors.

The typical features of the modern commercial world are thus about as follows. The landscape is dominated by the urban places, where most of the population lives. In the cities are concentrated facilities of manufacture, service, and communication. Within the countries where producers' economies are fully established, rural dwellers partake of most of the same living conditions as city folk. The country is traversed by a network of circulation routes, into which are fed raw materials from specialized sites of farming, forestry, mineral extraction, and fishing. The cities tend to be nearly alike; the rural regions, to differ in appearance because of specialization. A steady circulation also connects the metropolitan commercial countries with overseas outposts in which productive enterprises and cities form members of the same system. All commercial countries and their outposts are laced by the routes of circulation into one world.

Technologically, the commercial environment is distinctive. It represents the incorporation of more different natural substances into an artificial complex than are found under any other technical system. Likewise, much greater quantities of raw materials are extracted, under a producer's economy, than under any other economic order. The diversity of the means of production is unparalleled. The volume of inanimate power supply is incomparable. The intensity of circulation is unlike any known elsewhere or before, and the degree of linkage of interests and activities among places and peoples spatially distant from one another is unprecedented.

The modern inhabitant of a commercial country does not make his world; he buys it. The material circumstances of his life are not the outcome of his individual encounter with the natural order, but arise out of his relations with the social order.

The commercial form of organization, and the artificial habitats developed under it, tend to override differences of person and of place. They are anonymous and worldwide. Virtually all of the environment affecting individuals has become so modified that it represents a special and very peculiar set of living conditions. It is still nature, but nature tamed. The climates under which individuals actually live are closely regulated by artificial means within the buildings and vehicles where they spend most of their lives. The food they eat, the water they drink, and even the air they breathe, are provided to them through technical devices. The continuous and heavy circulation of goods and persons and ideas nourishes the settlements and maintains their people.

The artificial environment, created and continued by the efforts of the whole society, is the new harvesting ground of consumers, who stalk through its shopping districts gathering manufactured and transported products as the nomad Semang prowl the forest in quest of natural products. Modern consumers are utterly dependent on the exchange system. The wealth or poverty of nature in the immediate surroundings, and the rhythm of the seasons, are indifferent for their modes of consumption. The natural controls on human life, while still in effect, are equalized and regularized over time and space.

The circulation of commodities upon which finally rests the whole commercial symbiosis cannot proceed without a continual intake of natural materials and energies from resource sites and cultivated lands. Although the development of all the rest of the productive system may be almost entirely under the control of human ingenuity and effort, the extraction of raw materials cannot occur except where natural conditions are propitious. Resource endowments thus impose potential limits on production and on the possible development of artificial environments.

A new order of relationships between the earth and man arises with the establishment of the producers' economy. Whatever natural site or substance can be of use, no matter where it is located, becomes potentially subject to exploitation by whoever can use it. Whatever wants consumers anywhere experience or can be encouraged to develop evoke further production and resource use. Improved technical means allow a higher rate of resource extraction. Specialized industries develop very particular requirements for certain materials in great quantities. More favorable artificial environments favor rapid growth of populations and rising standards of consumption.

This way of life and this peculiar artificial world we live in are remarkably unlike any other system for living that man has produced. They are so familiar that one must adopt a very detached point of view to see all of their peculiarity. Yet the order under which we live is still akin to all the other ways of human life. It will be well to review and to compare them all now and to take stock of the evidence they afford as to man's role on earth, its opportunities, and its limitations.

A GEOGRAPHIC
OUTLOOK

MAN IS EVERYWHERE and always a social being and a user
of artifacts. He works to recreate the world. Learning, exploring,
inventing, saving, building, and planning, he contrives to make
nature serve his will. Not only does the social habit enable
men to work together for common ends; not only is the human
body, especially when armed with tools, a very efficient working
unit; above all, through culture men achieve the capacity to
change, improve, and adapt both their own behavior and the
physical world around them. Man's ability to consider and to
change himself sets him apart from all other creatures, and
equips him to dominate the earth.

Diversity of cultural inheritance underlies the differences
in the ways of working, of using artifacts and of organizing
shown in human societies and expressed materially in their
respective environments. However, one finds relatively few possible patterns for human livelihood, fundamental classes of

artifacts, and basic forms of economic organization. The several livelihood patterns, kinds of artifacts, and economic forms tend to appear in any given society and culture cumulatively, rather than successively and separately.[1] This fact permits comparison among societies in regard to these features.

A RECAPITULATION

THE VISIBLE DIFFERENCES among the regions of the earth, insofar as they can be attributed to human influence rather than to natural circumstances, express the distribution of certain ecological, cultural, and social characteristics among various human populations. Principal among these are the mechanisms of food supply, the organization of economic life, and the technical means of production—all of which are registered in artificial features of environment.

Man, like other animals, is dependent on the photo-synthesizing plants. The human food supply is always based upon a symbiotic complex of which green plants are members. The simplest form of this symbiosis is not mutualistic because it involves no dependence of wild plants and game upon their human users. Sometimes human groups make general use of many different wild plants and animals; at other times and places, however, they depend upon a few given species.

When man cultivates plants and domesticates animals, he is bound in a mutualistic relationship with them. The plants and animals both depend on care from man and serve to satisfy his wants. These symbioses always involve but a few species which are selected and specialized for life under human husbandry. Some human groups depend upon a close symbiosis with herds of domestic animals, which pasture under their watch upon wild vegetation; in other cases, groups grow crop plants to feed the domestic animals upon which man feeds.

We observe still other forms of symbiosis in which a human group which does not produce food is linked with food-producers, and, through them, with animals and plants. This symbiosis is a feature of certain forms of economic organization, and is the foundation for urban life and specialized services and manufactures.

An economy is an arrangement relating productive activity with consumption. The scope of the unit of economic organization varies from a single family household to a great state. Both the functions of "firms" or producers' groups, and those of the consuming "households" are governed by the economy. A single household and a single firm may coincide in a household economy, or a multitude of great productive enterprises and countless small consumer units may be encompassed within one national economy.

People either "make a living" or "earn a living." Under subsistence economies, a small group of persons, ordinarily of family size, produces only for its own consumption and consumes only what it produces. Under an exchange economy, households do not produce what they consume, nor consume what they produce. Their members work to earn entitlement to goods and services. An intermediate arrangement is the peasant economy; under it, the family or other small unit produces its own food supply and also exchanges a portion of its produce to satisfy other wants. In a peasant economy, there are always both rural and urban sectors, i.e., both food-producers and specialists in other activities who do not produce food.

Exchange takes three forms: redistribution, reciprocity, and market. In redistribution, control of the goods and services produced is centralized, and a central agency reapportions them to consumers. Reciprocal and market exchange are not thus centrally directed. In the former, trading is governed by the respective statuses and traditional prerogatives of the partners in exchange; in the latter, the market is operated according to the principle of equivalent value of commodities. Traders in markets may employ either barter—exchange in kind—or money, but only when they use money can exchange become very flexible and widespread.

Exchange relations that affect only finished goods characterize a consumers' economy. In a producers' economy, exchange intervenes in the productive process, and active markets arise for land (with its natural raw materials and energies), for capital, and for labor. The consumers' economy is often associated with peasant situations; the producers' economy is associated with and makes possible rationalized production.

Man as producer is distinguished by his propensity to create the means of further production as well as to work for satisfaction of his immediate wants. Productive artifacts extend the effect of bodily organs, magnify and translate human motions, furnish power to obey man's guidance, inform the human senses about the world, confine and control the motion of objects and substances, and carry other objects. They transmit or restrict motion, and introduce man's influence into the moving realms of nature.

Artifacts which function simply to transmit a motion imparted by the user are tools; those which merely contain or channel some material are facilities. Most productive artifacts are compounds of tools with facilities. Machines, combining features of both, have moving parts that translate motion; prime movers and similar devices make available inanimate energy to drive power-machines; automatic machines incorporate instruments and controls and can regulate their own performance. Vehicles, water, and aircraft are facilities that move; machines often furnish them with special sources of power.

An altogether different category of "means of production" is the complex of plants, animals, fields, gardens, pastures and other material features associated with cultivation. Domestic plants and animals and cultivated plots are associated with a particular symbiotic relationship. According to the spatial pattern it follows, cultivation is permanent, rotating, and intermittent or shifting.

Cultivation, even if it be intermittent, implies more or less fixed settlements. Fixed settlements are found, too, among peoples who do not have domestic plants, but make intensive use of abundant wild animals and plants of a few species, and who preserve and store large quantities of them. Nomadism, in contrast, is the habit of groups that gather a wide variety of natural goods and consume them directly. It is also the way of life of some pastoral peoples who, however, carry with them abundant impedimenta, and drive along the herds that feed them. Urban populations dependent for food upon the cultivators inhabit the largest fixed settlements of all. In some instances, however, these settlements and their countrysides are served by an unprecedented circulation of people and commodities, and hardly can be called sedentary systems. Under producers' economies a distinctive "circulatory" regime can be recognized in places in addition to the nomadic and the sedentary regimes.

Each individual combination of particular features of food supply, economy, techniques and spatial order that occurs in some human group tends to constitute the basis for distinctive ways of using an environment and modifying it for human use. The effect of the interaction of a human group with its environment tends to be registered most prominently at certain places reserved to particular activities. By virtue of frequent or constant use by man, these sites and routes of activity are prominently marked out as artificial features. A system of such features, more or less clearly impressed upon the land, diagrams the work and living patterns of the people.

The sites and routes of activity consist of the places where natural resources are exploited, the lines along which traffic and communication flow, the cultivated lands, the manufacturing plants, the centers at which services—public, professional, and private—are available, and the settlements and temporary dwelling places. Not everywhere, to be sure, are representatives of all these types in evidence. Every society exploits some resources and occupies some dwelling sites and uses routes of circulation; but for some human groups, the cultivated lands are lacking, and such manufactures and services as exist are carried on wherever opportunity permits.

COMPARISONS AND INFERENCES

AS EXAMPLES of distinctive artificial environments we may take the cases of some groups in Mexico. In the Seri country of southern Sonora, the entire modification achieved by the natives, who were nomadic gatherers and fishermen, consisted of a network of desert trails scarcely discernible to any but the Seri themselves, some refuse heaps where families had camped or feasted on shellfish, an occasional cache of food or water, and the littered campsite. In the mountains of Oaxaca, where the people are intermittent subsistence cultivators, the patchy disturbance of the vegetation shows their touch. Cultivated plots are evident. Thatched villages with whitewashed public buildings stand out. Rough but passable trails wind through the hills. Not far distant, however, in the Valley of Mexico, the smokestacks of factories contribute their share of particles to the general haze. Airplanes drone in the sky, and trucks and buses whiz along the highways. The countryside around the city is strewn with refuse and dotted with countless pepper trees, an imported species,[2] and with crumbling adobe walls and battered buildings. Day and night, there is traffic on the roads. At night lights are dim and distant in the country, bright and colorful in the city. The Valley here and there has bright green spots where maize is growing. One senses that a larger world stretches off continuously beyond.

These striking differences of environment reflect above all the dissimilarity of the societies concerned. The faint tracks and middens and dead campfires of wanderers like the Seri; the isolated but elaborate camps and small villages of sedentary collectors and traveling hunters; the charred and slashed fields, scrubby regrowth vegetation, and dusty hamlets of the shifting cultivators; the carefully tended fields, crowded villages, and busy thoroughfares of a peasant people are similar wherever found. The modern urban centers are perhaps even more alike everywhere than these, and so are the farms and mines and ports and railroads and factories of commercial countries.

The addition of certain critical artificial features to a group's environment reflects cultural advance and permits increases in the regularity and abundance of the livelihood. A people chained to a continual round of gathering wild products, which possesses few skills and carries few artifacts, has small effect upon its surroundings. Folk who make tools and permanent dwellings can accumulate supplies of food and expand their material wealth by manufacture. Cultivation of the land brings yet other advantages, for it reduces the distances covered in production, and provides a food supply more abundant and secure. Routes and markets serving commerce facilitate exchange of crops for manufactured goods; the peasant secures welcome aids to work; the craftsman, outlets for his wares. The urban centers and communication lines required in profusion for establishment of full producers' economies open the way to a vast increase in the circulation of commodities, and the scale of productive operations grows tremendously as a result.

The present contrasts among societies in regard to certain of these critical features need not be taken as derived from single historical events. The decisive changes leading to cultural growth and material advancement probably accumulate gradually; and there must be many minor influences as well as the major ones here considered. Furthermore, the trends have not remained uniform. Nomadism, for example, recurs after the development of sedentary life, and probably after agriculture. The gathering of wild products and predation by man grow in volume in the industrial age. The older or more elementary forms continue to appear, because advance is cumulative: industrial engineers and managers hunt, fish, camp, and garden.

The growth of productive capacity through the successive improvements of sedentary manufacture and accumulation, cultivation of the soil, commercial exchange, and the urban-industrial order, is accompanied by other improvements and advantages. Every advance in shelter or food supply, and every measure of sanitation or defense, may promote the health and longevity of individuals and the survival and increase of the population. Opportunities for experiment and invention increase. At each step, more time becomes available for reflection and creative effort, and more material means (i.e., "surplus") become expendable for technical investigations and artistic expression. Social differentiation progressively increases. Even the conduct of warfare becomes steadily more serious and efficient.

A major change in the character of the artificial environment produces its effect upon the conditions of life for man. The expansion of the artificial component of habitat at the expense of the natural portion ordinarily results in an enhancement of man's material well-being and in an increase, in time, of human population. Despite the frequent ugliness and waste attendant on man's interference in his natural surroundings, the general upward trend of human prosperity and population increase indisputably runs with, and not against, the trend of rapid growth in man's physical powers and influence in nature.

The establishment of new artificial conditions calls forth a proliferation of auxiliary and subsidiary changes. Each step of the development is conditioned upon preceding steps, and in its turn becomes the basis for succeeding advances. A definite order and proportion are to be observed in the growth of artificial complexes. The course of material development is thus to a considerable degree inherently limited by the specific requirements and capacities of the developing complex itself. The operation of the installations and equipment making up the complex also continues to depend upon proper balance and coordination throughout. A sufficient disturbance or destruction of some essential part of an artificial complex, correspondingly, induces disruption or disaster for the whole.

The human purposes of an artificial complex, and its own internal character, further interact with natural conditions to limit its development and operation.[3] Technical production requirements for space, materials, and energy are highly specific. The location of any artificial feature is likewise under limitations of physical and biotic circumstances, which thus exert a limiting effect upon the entire complex. A modern industrial system, for example, must include coal and iron mines; if suitable mineral deposits are not present within a country, it must link itself economically with countries where they do exist. The varied, exacting and voluminous requirements of industry in technically advanced countries are, in fact, such as to create a multitude of interdependent relationships among nations. The urban industrial countries have had to diffuse their economic and technical arrangements throughout the world in order to find the proper natural circumstances for situating certain essential members of their artificial complex of sites and routes. The attendant growth of circulation and the volume of extraction of raw materials and agricultural products, as well as the resulting involvement of all nations and peoples in common enterprises and close interaction, create for man new opportunities, problems, and conflicts on a world scale.

CONCLUSIONS AND OBSERVATIONS

CERTAIN PROPOSITIONS that emerge out of the discussion may be set forth here:

1. The relation of man to his natural environment is always mediated by artificial agencies.

2. The frequency, variety, and magnitude of the geographic features produced by human activity express the degree of artificiality attained by the group.

3. The security and independence of human groups with relation to natural circumstances are roughly proportional to the degree of artificial control the respective groups are able to exert.

4. The density of human populations and the spatial scope of societal organization are roughly proportional to the degree of artificiality attained by the given group.

5. A close and readily demonstrable interdependence and parity exists among the forms of societal organization, economic integration, technical equipment and capabilities, and spatial order characteristic of different human groups.

6. The increase of artificial control of nature by man is related to increasing variety and elaboration of the symbiotic relationships in which men participate.

7. Differences and deficiencies among natural environments may be overcome by artificial means.

8. Differences in human welfare are much more closely correlated with differences in artificial environments than with differences of natural environment.

9. Increasing artificiality favors intense regional specialization of production, and at the same time a widening generalization of consumption patterns. The widespread but small-scale use of relatively poor and varied local resources gives way to the concentrated use of fewer but more favorable resource sites, and

poor and varied local commodities are replaced by standardized goods and services of higher quality.

10. The progression that takes place in social relations is one from virtual independence of small groups to vast interdependence among peoples and places.

11. Natural, societal, and technical factors all exercise some control over every single element in an artificial environment and so over the whole artificial complex.

12. There are necessary *natural limitations* to the security, stability, and success of artificial environments. The ratio between supplies of essential natural resources and the number of consumers is critical. In a universally interdependent artificial system, the failure of a few resources could be sufficient to imperil any one of the many specialized functions that are indispensable to the operation of the whole.

13. *Societal limitations* likewise assert themselves. A depression, strike, plague, or revolution can impede the operation of some essential part of the artificial system and endanger the welfare or survival of a nation or ultimately of humanity.

14. *Technical limitations* exist, too, and are such that, for example, an appropriate military strategy could, by destroying or neutralizing a few well-chosen targets, halt some essential function and paralyze a nation.

15. The very original role of man in nature is consequent upon the biological peculiarities of the human species. Man is inherently a restless remaker of his own world.

NOTES

1. The most detailed exposition of professional geographic thought available in English is found in Richard Hartshorne, *The Nature of Geography; A Critical Survey of Current Thought in the Light of the Past* (Lancaster, Pa.: Association of American Geographers, 1939); and the same author's *Perspective on the Nature of Geography* (Chicago: Rand-McNally & Co., 1959. Association of American Geographers, "Monograph Series," No. 1.) Also see Edward A. Ackerman, *Geography as a Fundamental Research Discipline* (University of Chicago, Department of Geography, Research Paper No. 53, 1958); Norton S. Ginsburg, "Geography," in Bert F. Hoselitz (ed.), *A Reader's Guide to the Social Sciences* (Glencoe, Ill.: The Free Press, 1959), pp. 70-88; Preston E. James and Clarence F. Jones (eds.), *American Geography: Inventory and Prospect* (Syracuse, N. Y.: Syracuse University Press, 1954); and Griffith Taylor (ed.), *Geography in the Twentieth Century* (3rd ed.; New York:

Philosophical Library; London: Methuen, 1957). The related German thought is set out in Alfred Hettner, *Die Geographie: ihre Geschichte, ihr Wesen, und ihre Methoden* (Breslau: Ferdinand Hirt, 1927).

2. The limitations of the regional method were already made clear by Camille Vallaux in *Les sciences géographiques* (Paris: Felix Alcan, 1929).

3. There are numerous texts, treatises, and monographs in physical geography. See, for example, Arthur N. Strahler, *Physical Geography* (New York: John Wiley & Sons, Inc.; London: Chapman and Hall, 1951), which contains also many references to the literature of the field.

4. A good idea of what has been done and what is being done toward developing more general theories of geographic order may be formed on the basis of these books: Edgar M. Hoover, *The Location of Economic Activity* (New York: McGraw-Hill Book Co., Inc., 1948); Walter Isard, *Location and Space Economy* (New York: John Wiley & Sons, Inc., 1956); August Lösch, *The Economics of Location,* trans. W. H. Woglom with the assistance of W. F. Stolper (New Haven: Yale University Press, 1954); and William Warntz, *Toward a Geography of Price* (Philadelphia: University of Pennsylvania Press; London: Oxford University Press, 1959). Two useful review articles covering the recent literature are Brian J. L. Berry, "Recent Studies Concerning the Role of Transportation in the Space Economy," *Annals of the Association of American Geographers,* XLIX (September, 1959), 328-42, and William Warntz, "Contributions Toward a Macroeconomic Geography: A Review," *Geographical Review,* XLVII (July, 1957), 420-24. Some important articles and books dealing with special topics in location are: Edward L. Ullman, *American Commodity Flow; A Geographical Interpretation of Rail and Water Traffic Based on Principles of Spatial Interchange* (Seattle: University of Washington Press, 1957); Chauncy D. Harris, "The Market as a Factor in the Localization of Industry in the United States," *Annals of the Association of American Geographers,* XLIV, No. 4 (1954), 315-48; Edward L. Ullman, "A Theory of Location for Cities," *American Journal of Sociology,* XLVI, No. 6 (1941), 853-64; and Charles T. Stewart, Jr., "The Size and Spacing of Cities," *Geographical Review,* XLVIII (April, 1958), 222-45.

5. The use of these concepts in this book resembles that of behaviorist and Gestalt psychology. Cf. Kenneth W. Spence, "The Postulates and Methods of Behaviorism," *Psychological Review,* LV (1948), reprinted in Herbert Feigl and May Brodbeck (eds.), *Readings in the Philosophy of Science* (New York: Appleton-Century-Crofts, Inc., 1953), pp. 571-84. The implication of simple stimulus and response, if transferred at all to the phenomena to be discussed herein, should refer to the whole technical system, of course, and not to individual human beings or to societal units per se.

The philosophical background of this book may be sought in particular in J. H. Woodger, *Biological Principles: A Critical Study* (London: Routledge and Kegan Paul Ltd., 1929) and S. F. Nadel, *Foundations of Social Anthropology* (Glencoe, Ill.: The Free Press, 1957).

6. On the environmentalist issue, see especially Lucien Febvre, *La terre et l'évolution humaine; introduction géographique à l'histoire* (Paris: Albin Michel, 1922), also available in English as *A Geographical Introduction to History* (New York, 1925); two articles by Robert S. Platt: "Environmentalism Versus Geography," *American Journal of Sociology*, LIII, 1948, 351-58, and "Determinism in Geography," *Annals of the Association of American Geographers*, XXXVIII (1948), 126-28; and Erhard Rostlund, "Twentieth Century Magic," *Landscape*, V (Spring, 1956), 23-26. The history of environmentalist thought in geography is recounted briefly in G. Tatham, "Environmentalism and Possibilism," in Griffith Taylor (ed.), *Geography in the Twentieth Century* (2d ed.; New York: Philosophical Library; London: Methuen & Co., Ltd., 1953), pp. 128-62. The role of the environmentalist doctrine in sociology is described in Franklin Thomas, *The Environmental Basis of Society; A Study in the History of Sociological Theory* (New York and London: Century, 1925). The only full philosophical study devoted to this matter seems to be Émile Callot, *La société et son environnement. Essai sur les principes des sciences sociales* (Paris: Marcel Rivière, 1952). See also Carl Hempel, "The Function of General Laws in History," *Journal of Philosophy*, XXXIX (1942), reprinted in Herbert Feigl and W. Sellars (eds.), *Readings in Philosophical Analysis* (New York: Appleton-Century-Crofts Inc., 1949), pp. 459-71, esp. p. 470. A rebuttal from the neo-determinist standpoint, Emrys Jones, "Cause and Effect in Human Geography," *Annals of the Association of American Geographers*, XLVI (December 1956), 367-77, is compatible with the viewpoint of this book.

7. The term "artificial" has often been used in this connection. Ernst Kapp, in his *Grundriss einer Philosophie der Technik* (Braunschweig: Westermann, 1877), wrote of "des Menschen artefaktische Aussenwelt" (p. 343). Bronislaw Malinowski, in his *A Scientific Theory of Culture and Other Essays* (Chapel Hill: University of North Carolina Press, 1944), uses both the terms "artificial" and "secondary" for environments made by man. The usual terms in geography in the United States have been "cultural" as against "natural" landscapes, a distinction introduced here by Carl O. Sauer in *The Morphology of Landscape* ("University of California Publications in Geography," No. 2, Berkeley and Los Angeles, 1925).

8. The implications of mobility patterns for social organization have often been remarked, but not, so far as I know, followed out. See, for example, Hettner, *op. cit.*, p. 197; Amos O. Hawley, *Human*

Ecology; A Theory of Community Structure (New York: Ronald Press Co., 1950), p. 293; and especially Richard K. Beardsley *et al.*, "Functional and Evolutionary Implications of Community Patterning," *Memoirs of the Society for American Archaeology*, No. 11 (1956), 129-57 in *American Antiquity*, XXII, no. 2, Part II. This idea was carried to greater lengths by some early French sociologists, of whose writings Edmond Demolins, *Les grandes routes des peuples. Essai de géographie sociale. Comment la route crée le type social* (2 vols.; Paris: Firmin-Didot, 1901) is perhaps the most striking. Cf. the comments on this book in L. Febvre, *op. cit.*

9. Notice Hans Reichenbach's remarks on the "reality" of time and space in *The Rise of Scientific Philosophy* (Berkeley and Los Angeles: University of California Press, 1951), pp. 139 and 154-55, respectively.

CHAPTER TWO

Conditions of Human Life

1. A very considerable literature exists on the subjects of bioclimatology and meteorobiology. See: August Seybold and Heinz Woltereck (eds.), *Klima, Wetter, Mensch* (Heidelberg: Quelle & Meyer, 1952); Manfred Curry, *Bioclimatologie: die Steuerung des gesunden und kranken Organismus durch die Atmosphäre* (Riederau/Ammersee: American Bioclimatic Research Institute, 1946); and Bernhard de Rudder, *Grundriss einer Meteorobiologie des Menschen; Wetter und Jahreszeiteneinflüsse*, Third "neubearbeitete Auflage" (Berlin: Springer, 1952). A valuable work at more general level is Lev S. Berg, *Klimat i zhizn'* ("Climate and Life") (2d ed.; Moscow: "Geografizdat," 1947).

2. On somatic modifications among Peruvian Indians, mostly in physiology only, see Carlos Monge, "Biological Basis of Human Behavior," in A. L. Kroeber (ed.), *Anthropology Today; an Encyclopedic Inventory* (Chicago: University of Chicago Press, 1953), pp. 127-44, with an extensive bibliography of Peruvian work.

3. An extended discussion of the geographical distribution of human morphological features, with some remarks on their possible origin, is found in R. Biasutti, "I caratteri morfologici," in R. Biasutti (ed.), *Le razze e i popoli della terra* (Torino: Unione Tipografico-editrice Torinese, 1959), I, 189-256. In the four volumes of this work produced by Italian scholars, there is perhaps more information upon the morphological features of human populations in their geographic distribution than can be found in any other single place.

Stanley A. Garn, in "Race and Evolution," *American Anthropologist,* LIX (April 1957), 218-24, argues that adaptive changes in the genetic constitution of human races are proceeding at the present under selection pressure. He points especially to studies of Rh and A-B-O factors of the blood. Some of the mechanisms involved are identified by John Buettner-Janusch in "Natural Selection in Man; The ABO(H) Blood Group System," *American Anthropologist,* LXI (June 1959), 437-56. Work on somatic modifications in children of immigrants, in which the observed changes have been attributed mostly to dietary and similar influences rather than to climate, is reviewed in Bernice A. Kaplan, "Environment and Human Plasticity," *American Anthropologist,* LVI (October 1954), 780-800.

4. See Douglas H. K. Lee, "Physiological Climatology," in Preston E. James and Clarence F. Jones (eds.), *American Geography; Inventory and Prospect* (Syracuse, N. Y.: Syracuse University Press, 1954), pp. 470-83.

5. The nature and consequences of catastrophes are treated in L. Don Leet, *Causes of Catastrophe: Earthquakes, Volcanoes, Tidal Waves, and Hurricanes* (New York: McGraw-Hill Book Co., 1948). A brief treatment, with good bibliographic references on special topics, is found in Richard J. Russell, "Environmental Changes Through Forces Independent of man," in William L. Thomas, Jr. (ed.), *Man's Role in Changing the Face of the Earth* (Chicago: University of Chicago Press, 1956), pp. 453-70.

6. Reliable data on minimal food requirements are hard to come by. The information available is summarized in Max Sorre, *Les fondements de la géographie humaine,* "Les fondements biologiques" (Paris: Armand Colin, 1951), Tome I, pp. 219-46, including a bibliography. See also the brief discussion and references in Marvin Harris, "The Economy Has No Surplus?," *American Anthropologist,* LXI (April 1959), 185-99.

Sorre's succeeding chapter, *op. cit.,* pp. 247-90, as well as the following works, are pertinent to the question of actual diets of the past and present: A. Maurizio, *Histoire de l'alimentation végétale depuis la préhistoire jusqu'à nos jours* (Paris: Payot, 1932); Michel Cépède and Maurice Lengellé, *Économie alimentaire du globe; essai d'interprétation* (Paris: Librairie de Médicis, 1953); Josué de Castro, *La alimentación en los trópicos* (Mexico: Fondo de Cultura Económica, 1946); Karl Sapper, *L'alimentation de l'humanité. Son économie, sa répartition, ses possibilités,* trans. Georges Montandon (Paris: Payot, 1942); and B. L. Jensen, *Man's Foods; Nutrition and Environments in Food Gathering and Food Producing Times* (Champaign, Ill.: Garrard Press, 1953).

7. *The Ecology of Human Disease,* by Jacques May (New York: MD Publications, 1959), is a particularly good source of information on the geographical aspects of medicine.

8. Definitions of "obligate," "facultative," and "symbiosis" as used in biology are given in R. J. Carpenter, *An Ecological Glossary* (Norman: University of Oklahoma Press, 1938).

9. See Edgar Anderson, "Man as a Maker of New Plants and New Plant Communities," and Marston Bates, "Man as an Agent in the Spread of Organisms," both in Thomas, *op. cit.*, pp. 763-77 and 788-804, respectively, where the discussions and bibliographies lead off into a rich and curious realm of ideas.

10. An article by Carl O. Sauer, "Theme of Animal and Plant Destruction in Economic History," *Journal of Farm Economics*, XX (1938), 765-75, presents the case for extinction of many large species of mammals through human agency.

11. A series of articles in Thomas, *op. cit.*, documents some of the great changes that have taken place in vegetation under man's influence. They are: Omer C. Stewart, "Fire as the First Great Force Employed by Man," pp. 115-39; Fritz M. Heichelheim, "Effects of Classical Antiquity on the Land," pp. 165-82; H. C. Darby, "The Clearing of the Woodland in Europe," pp. 183-216; Hermann von Wissman *et al.*, "On the Role of Nature and Man in Changing the Face of the Dry Belt of Asia," pp. 278-303; Soliman Huzayyin, "Changes in Climate, Vegetation, and Human Adjustment in the Saharo-Arabian Belt, With Special Reference to Africa," pp. 304-23; Pierre Gourou, "The Quality of Land Use of Tropical Cultivators," pp. 336-49; James C. Malin, "The Grassland of North America; Its Occupance and the Challenge of Continuous Reappraisals," pp. 350-66; H. H. Bartlett, "Fire, Primitive Agriculture, and Grazing in the Tropics," pp. 692-720; John T. Curtis, "The Modification of Mid-latitude Grasslands and Forests by Man," pp. 721-36; Andrew H. Clark, "The Impact of Exotic Invasion on the Remaining New World Mid-latitude Grasslands," pp. 737-62; and F. Frazer Darling, "Man's Ecological Dominance through Domesticated Animals on Wild Lands," pp. 778-87.

A pioneer observer of man's effect on vegetation was O. F. Cook, whose classic analysis was "Vegetation Affected by Agriculture in Central America" (U. S. Department of Agriculture, Bureau of Plant Industry, Bulletin No. 145 [Washington, D.C.: 1909]). Sauer generalizes on this theme in "Early Relations of Man ·to Plants," *Geographical Review*, XXXVII (1942), 1-25.

12. On the microclimate of buildings, cf. Lee, *op. cit.*, and Rudolf Geiger, *The Climate Near the Ground*, trans. Milroy N. Stewart, *et al.* (Cambridge, Mass.: Harvard University Press, 1950), pp. 386-95.

13. Cf. Lee, *op. cit.*

14. There is a large literature, chiefly polemical, upon the theme of declining resources and growing populations. Some modern examples are Harrison Brown, *The Challenge of Man's Future* (New York: Viking Press, 1954); Fairfield Osborn, *The Limits of the*

Earth (Boston: Little, Brown and Co., 1953), and *Our Plundered Planet* (Boston: Little, Brown and Co., 1948); William Vogt, *The Road to Survival* (New York: William Sloane Associates, 1948), all of which state the pessimistic side of the issue. Earl Parker Hanson, *New Worlds Emerging* (New York: Duell, Sloan & Pearce, Inc., 1949) and Josue de Castro, *The Geography of Hunger* (Boston: Little, Brown and Co., 1952) are more optimistic.

CHAPTER THREE

Man's Place in the World

1. Sauer's address, "Foreword to Historical Geography," *Annals of the Association of American Geographers*, XXXI, No. 1 (1941), 1-24, from which this remark is taken, offers a fine exposition of his very influential ideas upon questions of human geography.

2. This principle is a cornerstone of Barrows' philosophy as expressed in "Geography as Human Ecology," *Annals of the Association of American Geographers*, XIII, No. 1 (1923), 1-14, which, for some reason, had but slight echo in later methodological writing in geography. Hartshorne, incorrectly I think, cites Barrows' address as an outstanding example of environmentalism, and attempts to refute its reasoning (*The Nature of Geography* . . . , 1938, p. 123). Compare Barrows' words with those of Camille Vallaux: "Ce sont les indices de travail que nous permettent de compléter les expressions de quantité au moyen d'un classement rationnel des groupes humains qui font sentir, en tant que groupes, leur action sur le sol, qui déforment les paysages d'une manière qui leur est propre et qui parviennent à créer dans son ensemble le quatrième état de la matière." *Les sciences géographiques* . . . (1929), p. 203.

3. Cf. Hartshorne, *op. cit.*, p. 468: "The ultimate purpose of geography [is] the study of areal differentiation of the world."

4. The concept of culture will be treated below, pp. 34 ff.

5. The idea of human action within the system of physical nature is masterfully treated in a paper of George Herbert Mead appearing in *The Philosophy of the Act*, Charles W. Morris *et al.* (eds.) (Chicago: University of Chicago Press, 1938), especially pp. 412-43. A considerable part of the inspiration for the present work was drawn from reading Mead.

6. This statement is from a highly original and stimulating book by H. Hediger, director of the Basel zoo: *Wild Animals in Captivity; An Outline of the Biology of Zoological Gardens* (London: Butterworth & Co., 1950), p. 9. See also his *Studies in the Psychology and*

Behavior of Captive Animals in Zoos and Circuses (New York: Criterion Books, Inc., 1955). The spatial behavior of animals is described in many other works, among which may be cited in particular F. Bourliere, *The Natural History of Mammals* (2d ed.; New York: Alfred A. Knopf Inc., 1956), esp. pp. 103-7. This book contains a large and valuable bibliography on mammalian behavior.

By far the best general reference on animal ecology, and the standard work, is W. C. Allee, Orlando Park, Alfred E. Emerson, Thomas Park, and Karl P. Schmidt, *Principles of Animal Ecology* (Philadelphia: W. B. Saunders Co., 1949).

7. For territoriality in mammals, see Bourliere, *op. cit.*, pp. 94-107. Similar patterns are found among birds and often among fish.

8. The artifacts used by animals are described in *ibid.*, pp. 67-94.

9. The concept of the community is one of the foundations of modern ecology, and is treated in all recent textbooks on the subject.

10. W. C. Allee, *Animal Aggregations; A Study in General Sociology* (Chicago: University of Chicago Press, 1931), describes the many types of aggregations of one or several species.

11. Communication in some species of bees is remarkable in its development, however. See Karl von Frisch, *Bees; Their Vision, Chemical Sense, and Language* (Ithaca, N. Y.: Cornell University Press, 1950), in which the ingenious discovery of a bee "language" based on perceptions of polarized sunlight, gravitational force, and bodily motion, is described.

12. For a thorough discussion of "culture," consult A. L. Kroeber and Clyde Kluckhohn, *Culture: A Critical Review of Concepts and Definitions*, "Peabody Museum Papers" (Cambridge, Mass.: Harvard University Press, 1952), Vol. XLVIII.

CHAPTER FOUR

Human Societies as Geographic Forms

1. Edmund Ronald Leach, in his *Political Systems of Highland Burma; A Study of Kachin Social Structure* (London: London School of Economics, 1954), shows this overall linkage convincingly. He also demonstrates that "cultural," linguistic, religious, social, kinship, economic, and political distinctions among groups may not coincide. This study of relations among Kachin hill peoples and valley-dwelling Shans demonstrates an overall political process and numerous bonds and divisions of every sort within a territory of considerable human diversity. The well-known case of the pastoral peoples of the Eurasian steppes also comes to mind as an instance of fragmentation of a

population in some respects (linguistic, economic, technical) simultaneous with politico-military, social and even kinship integration. On the questions treated in this chapter, a reading of Karl W. Deutsch, *Nationalism and Social Communication: An Inquiry into the Foundations of Nationality* (Cambridge, Mass.: Technology Press; New York: John A. Wiley & Sons, 1953) is strongly recommended.

2. The known cases of "feral children" and other possible exceptions to the general rule of human sociability are examined in Roger Brown, *Words and Things* (Glencoe, Ill.: The Free Press, 1958), pp. 186-92.

3. Cf. Philip L. Wagner, "Remarks on the Geography of Language," *Geographical Review*, XLVIII, No. 1 (1958), 86-97.

4. See A. Meillet and Marcel Cohen (eds.), *Les langues du monde* . . . (Paris: Centre National de la Recherche Scientifique, 1952) for details of language distribution and classification, including maps covering all parts of the world.

5. "Niger-Congo" is Greenberg's grouping, and is not universally accepted. See Joseph H. Greenberg, "Studies in African Linguistic Classification: VIII. Further Remarks on Method: Revisions and Conclusions," *Southwestern Journal of Anthropology*, X (Winter 1954), 405-15, with map.

6. The shift from Samoyedic to Turkic among the Sagai, Kacha, Soyot, and others is mentioned in W. K. Matthews, *Languages of the U.S.S.R.* (Cambridge: Cambridge University Press, 1951), p. 17. Russian has spread rapidly in the same area subsequently.

7. The relation of human to general vertebrate, especially mammalian, behavior is assessed very ably in Earl W. Count, "The Biological Basis of Human Sociality," *American Anthropologist*, LX (December, 1958), 1049-85.

8. A. L. Kroeber, "The Societies of Primitive Man," in Robert Redfield (ed.), *Levels of Integration in Biological and Social Systems*, "Biological Symposia" (Lancaster, Pa.: Cattell, 1942), VII, 205-16.

9. Bronislaw Malinowski, *Magic, Science and Religion and Other Essays* (Glencoe, Ill.: The Free Press, 1948), and, in particular, his demonstration of the place of magic in technical activities, in *Coral Gardens and Their Magic. A Study of the Method of Tilling the Soil and of Agricultural Rites in the Trobriand Islands* (London: Allen and Unwin Ltd., 1935).

10. Cf. Count, *op. cit.*, on the expansive qualities of statuses not based directly on kinship.

11. Charles P. Loomis, *Fundamental Concepts of Sociology* (New York: American Book Co., 1940) presents and discusses the original ideas of Tönnies, with a complete translation of his *Gemeinschaft und Gesellschaft* (Leipzig: Fues, 1887). See also, for related ideas, Robert Redfield, "The Folk Society," *American Journal of Sociology*,

LII (1947), 293-308, and Sir Henry Maine, *Ancient Law* (London: John Murray, 1861).

12. Robert Redfield, *The Primitive World and Its Transformations* (Ithaca, N. Y.: Cornell University Press, 1953).

13. *Ibid.*

14. Robert Redfield, *The Folk Culture of Yucatan* (Chicago: University of Chicago Press, 1941).

15. A good exposition of animal rank, with discussions of the work of Schjelderup-Ebbe, Allee, Carpenter, Tinbergen and others is presented in John Paul Scott, *Animal Behavior* (Chicago: University of Chicago Press, 1958), pp. 158-76.

16. The phenomenon of biological rank is treated in H. Hediger, *Studies of the Psychology and Behavior of Animals in Zoos and Circuses,* trans. Geoffrey Sircom (New York: Criterion Books Co., 1955), pp. 67 ff., upon which these remarks are based.

17. See F. Bourliere, *The Natural History of Mammals* (New York: Alfred A. Knopf Inc., 1956), pp. 66-107; and especially D. Lack, *The Natural Regulation of Animal Numbers* (Oxford: Clarendon Press, 1954).

18. On social rank see Hediger, *op. cit.,* pp. 67-87.

19. It is well to recall at this point Leach's cautions on the ambiguity of any single classification of human groups. Cf. note one, above.

20. Cf. Count, *op. cit.*

21. Derwent S. Whittlesey, *The Earth and the State; A Study of Political Geography* (New York: Henry Holt and Co., Inc., 1944), p. 2 ff.

22. This is the theme of organization of Robert S. Platt, *Latin America; Countrysides and United Regions* (New York: McGraw-Hill Book Co., Inc., 1942).

CHAPTER FIVE

The Economic Bond

1. "L'homme modifiant la nature à travers la technique, est aussi modifié par celle-ci à travers l'évolution des sociétés." Georges Friedmann, "Esquisse de quelques problèmes," *L'Homme, la technique, et la nature* (Paris: Rieder, 1938), p. 12.

2. The older idea of economic atomism is perhaps last expressed in Karl Bücher, *Die Entstehung der Volkswirtschaft; Vorträge und Aufsätze* (Tübingen: Laupp, 1925), Sammlung I, pp. 14 ff. It was amply refuted, among economic writers, by Max Schmidt, *Die soziale*

Organisation der menschlichen Wirtschaft "Grundriss der ethno-logischen Volkswirtschaftslehre, I" (Stuttgart: F. Enke, 1920), pp. 43-44; Werner von Sombart, *Der moderne Kapitalismus,* I (Leipzig: Duncker & Humblot, 1902), 10-11, 59 *passim.*

3. This point is well presented in Max Schmidt, *op. cit.,* esp. p. 47.

4. The dichotomy between "substantive" and "formal" economies is most explicitly discussed and most fully documented in Karl Polanyi, Conrad M. Arensberg, and Harry W. Pearson (eds.), *Trade and Market in the Early Empires; Economies in History and Theory* (Glencoe, Ill.: The Free Press and Falcon's Wing Press, 1957). Sombart, *op. cit.,* I, 15 ff, distinguishes between "Betrieb" or Arbeits-gemeinschaft (working unit) and "Wirtschaft" or Verwertungs-gemeinschaft (using unit). Max Schmidt, *op. cit.,* also separates the "materiale Wirtschaft," i.e., the "substantive economy" of Polanyi, from the "soziale Wirtschaft."

5. This distinction follows Sol Tax, *Penny Capitalism; A Guate-malan Indian Economy* (Smithsonian Institution. Institute of Social Anthropology Publication No. 16 [Washington, D.C., 1953]), p. 13.

6. *Op. cit.*

7. "Subsistence economy" here corresponds to the "individual economy" of Walter Eucken, *The Foundations of Economics; His-tory and Theory in the Analysis of Economic Reality,* trans. T. W. Hutchison (Chicago: University of Chicago Press, 1951), and Sombart, *op. cit.,* as well as with the "Gemeinwirtschaft mit Binnenverkehr" of Schmidt, the "closed economy" of Polanyi, and Karl Bücher's "geschlossene Hauswirtschaft."

8. This use of "exchange" differs, of course, from that of Eucken, who applies this name to what I shall designate as "market exchange."

9. Following Max Schmidt, these terms would correspond to "Verkehrswirtschaft mit Binnenverkehr" and "Verkehrswirtschaft mit Aussenverkehr," respectively, *op. cit.,* p. 127. Non-price, or closed exchange, can be equated with Sombart's "transitional economies" (Uebergangswirtschaften), *op. cit.,* I, 67, but I take merely price, rather than specifically profit (Erwerb) as the index of difference. Note also the possible correspondence to Bücher's "Stadtwirtschaft," if we interpret "Stadt" here as referring to a relatively closed com-munity rather than the open city; the word is ambiguous in German.

10. Cf. Polanyi *et al., op. cit.,* pp. 250 ff., for this and other ex-amples of his terminology here cited. The term appears in an earlier book of K. Polanyi, *The Great Transformation; The Political and Economic Origins of Our Time* (New York: Rinehart & Co., Inc., 1944), pp. 43 ff.

11. Cf. Eucken, *op. cit.,* pp. 120-22.

12. Neil J. Smelser, in a review of Polanyi *et al.,* "A Comparative

View of Exchange Systems," *Economic Development and Cultural Change*, VII (January, 1959), pp. 173-82, proposes the addition of a further category, "mobilizative" economy. I prefer to range this form under redistribution, because it is differentiated only by a particular purpose informing economic policy. Smelser's suggestion no doubt reflects special emphasis on contemporary economic development problems in his thinking, and the term "mobilizative" dissociates one group of essentially redistributive arrangements from the sometimes disagreeable associations of centralized economy as it is found historically.

13. In mentioning government as a redistributive phenomenon we expose the fact that these ideal economic forms are exemplified in reality within various combinations. Few, if any, societies are purely redistributive, and few lack this feature altogether.

14. "Market" is employed here in Polanyi's "formal" sense, i.e., not to mean a crowd in an actual marketplace, and as an approximate equivalent to the "Verkehrswirtschaft mit Aussenverkehr" of Max Schmidt, the "exchange" of Eucken, the "Gesellschaftswirtschaft" of Sombart, and (perhaps!) the "Volkswirtschaft" of Bücher. I do not, however, subscribe to Sombart's polarity of profit-making and subsistence economies (Erwerbswirtschaften and Bedarfsdeckungswirtschaften, respectively).

15. Polanyi's *The Great Transformation* . . . , is built around the thesis that a "self-regulating market" for land and labor, which is said to be the intended outcome of a relatively recent kind of development, cannot actually work successfully.

16. Eucken (*op. cit.*, p. 119), Sombart (*op. cit.*, I, 66), and Polanyi's school (Rotstein in Polanyi *et al.*, *op. cit.*, p. xviii) all properly claim that their somewhat differing classifications are "universal" or "exhaustive."

17. Transitional, that is, between "Individualwirtschaft" devoted to subsistence, and "Gesellschaftswirtschaft" serving profit. Sombart, *op. cit.*, I, 67.

18. Eucken, *op. cit.*, pp. 122-23, recognizes the possibility of a pure redistributive (literally "total central directed" in Hutchison's translation) economy, but suggests also two subtypes with "free exchange of consumer goods" and "freedom of consumer choice," respectively. These two subtypes seem to take care of almost any conceivable socialist, communist, incaic, or pharaonic redistributive system.

19. Cf. Malinowski, *Coral Gardens.* . . .

20. This often happens in times of crisis. Remember the Russian Revolution and the subsequent struggles to get grain for the cities which resulted in raids, turmoil, famine, and exile for the peasants. There was a hint of the same frantic situation in France and other

European countries just after World War II when the cities lacked food, but the peasants held back supplies, fearing a devaluation.

21. Restrictive tariffs and currency restrictions signify a recognition of this principle and a deliberate contravention of it.

22. The term "dual economy" is from J. H. Boeke, *The Structure of Netherlands Indian Economy* (New York: Institute of Pacific Relations, 1942).

23. Richard Thurnwald, *Economics in Primitive Communities* (London: Oxford University Press, 1937) and V. Gordon Childe, *What Happened in History* (Harmondsworth, Middlesex: Penguin, 1942).

24. C. Daryl Forde, *Habitat, Economy and Society; A Geographical Introduction to Ethnology* (London: Methuen & Co., 1934), see map, p. 5; Karl Sapper, *L'Alimentation de l'humanité* (Paris: Payot, 1942), chap. II, and map in appendix. Also see Derwent S. Whittlesey's various published classifications of "economies," the best known in the United States, and especially his "Major Agricultural Regions of the Earth," *Annals of the Association of American Geographers,* XXVI (1936), 199-240.

CHAPTER SIX

The Means of Production

1. Cf. Tadeusz Kotarbiński, *Traktat o dobrej robocie* (A Treatise on Good Work). (Lodz: Zaklad im. Ossolinskich, 1955), pp. 55-57, for differences between animal and human work.

2. Kenneth Oakley, *Man the Tool-maker* (Chicago: University of Chicago Press, 1957).

3. "While in appearance a machine differs greatly from any of the force- or motion-distributors of nature, yet for the theoretical or pure mechanician no such difference exists,—or rather it completely disappears on analysis, so that to him the problems of machinery fall into the same class as those of the mechanical phenomena of nature. He sees in both forces and motions existing, and subject to the same great laws which, developed in their most general form, govern and must govern every single case." Franz Reuleaux, *The Kinematics of Machinery: Outlines of a Theory of Machines,* trans. Alexander B. W. Kennedy (London: 1876), p. 29.

4. Stanley H. Udy, Jr., has made a pioneer effort to discover the relationships between societal features and technique, in his *Organization of Work; a Comparative Analysis of Production among Non-industrial Peoples* (New Haven: HRAF Press, 1959). His study

is based upon statistical treatment of ethnographic data. On the role played by energy use, see the stimulating study by William Frederick Cottrell, *Energy and Society: The Relations between Energy, Social Change, and Economic Development* (New York: McGraw-Hill Book Co., 1955).

5. Cf. Kotarbiński, *op. cit.*, pp. 36-57, for a similar point of view.

6. *Op. cit.*, p. 36.

7. "Man, in Nature, can only conquer her by first obeying her, by seeing and taking what in that place she gives and thereafter searching out what more he may be able to obtain from her. . . ." J. Arthur Thompson and Patrick Geddes, *Life; Outlines of a General Biology* (London: Williams & Norgate Ltd., 1931), I, p. 1393.

8. Kotarbiński makes this distinction. Lewis Mumford also distinguishes "containers" from other artifacts. Cf. his *Technics and Civilization* (New York: Harcourt, Brace & Co., 1934).

9. Probably the most comprehensive ethnographic classification is found in the two volumes of André Leroi-Gourhan, *L'Homme et la matière* (Paris: Albin Michel, 1943) and *Milieu et technique* (Paris: Albin Michel, 1945). There are many archaeological classifications, but apparently none on a comprehensive world scale, except for O. Menghin's *Weltgeschichte der Steinzeit* (Wien: A. Schroll, 1931).

10. See for example the chronologically arranged articles in Charles Singer, E. J. Holmyard, A. R. Hall and Trevor I. Williams (eds.), *A History of Technology* (5 Vols.; London: Oxford University Press, 1954-1959).

11. Certain mechanical devices of particular significance for the modern industrial system are studied in their historical development in Abbott Payson Usher, *A History of Mechanical Inventions* (rev. ed.; Cambridge, Mass.: Harvard University Press, 1954), which has an excellent bibliography. See also Lewis Mumford, *op. cit.*, and Siegfried Giedion, *Mechanization Takes Command: A Contribution to Autonomous History* (New York: Oxford University Press, 1948), both with ample bibliographies.

12. The arrangement which we shall use is in part based upon the works of Kotarbiński, *op. cit.;* Ernst Kapp, *Grundlinien einer Philosophie der Technik* (Braunschweig: G. Westermann, 1877), esp. pp. 57-61; L. Noiré, *Das Werkzeug und seine Bedeutung für die Entwicklungsgeschichte der Menschheit* (Mainz: J. Diemer, 1880), esp. pp. 259-61; Mumford, *op. cit.;* Reuleaux, *op. cit.;* and W. G. Waffenschmidt, *Technik und Wirtschaft* ("Grundrisse zum Studium der Nationalökonomie," Band 18 [Jena: Gustav Fischer, 1928]), and *Technik und Wirtschaft der Gegenwart* ("Enzyklopädie der Rechts- und Staatswissenschaft" [Berlin, Göttingen, Heidelberg: Springer, 1952]). Terminology has been standardized with that of *Chambers Technological Dictionary* wherever possible.

Waffenschmidt's categories, which are nearest to those used herein, are, with some of his examples: 1. *Werkzeug* (tool; exemplified by pedal-operated sewing machine); 2. *Maschinelles Werkzeug* (simple machine; *e.g.*, pressure screwdriver); 3. *Maschine;* 4. *Energieer-zeugungsmaschine,* combining *Kraftmaschine* and *Arbeitsmaschine* (power machine); 5. *Spezialmaschine* (for special purposes—roughly like a machine tool); 6. *Masswerkzeug* ("measuring tool," *i.e.*, instrument); 7. *Geräte* (device with no moving parts) and *Gehäuse* (a housing); and 8. *Apparat* (power operated instrument). Cf. *Technik und Wirtschaft der Gegenwart, op. cit.*, pp. 128-39.

13. See Leslie White, *The Science of Culture; a Study of Man and Civilization* (New York: Farrar & Strauss, 1949) for a statement of this standard thesis. William Frederick Cottrell, *op. cit.*, is the most thorough treatment of the subject.

14. Notice the restricted ranges and growing areas of crop plants, as mapped for instance in William Van Royen, *The Agricultural Resources of the World* ("Atlas of the World's Resources," Vol. I [New York: Prentice-Hall, 1954]).

15. The discussion in this section is in part based on the approach of Karl H. W. Klages, *Ecological Crop Geography* (New York: Macmillan Co., 1942). See also Sir E. John Russell, *Soil Conditions and Plant Growth* (8th ed. London: Longmans, Green & Co. Ltd., 1950).

16. The important distinction between seed and clone (or vegetatively reproduced) crops was pointed out by Carl O. Sauer. See his "Cultivated Plants of South and Central America," in Julian H. Steward (ed.), *Handbook of South American Indians* (Smithsonian Institution of Washington, Bureau of American Ethnology, Bulletin No. 143 [Washington: Smithsonian Institution, 1950]), VI, pp. 487-543; and C. O. Sauer, *Agricultural Origins and Dispersals* ("Bowman Memorial Lectures," series two [New York: American Geographical Society, 1952]).

17. See remarks on "domestic" characteristics in H. Hediger, *Studies in the Psychology and Behavior of Captive Animals in Zoos and Circuses,* trans. Geoffrey Sircom (New York: Criterion Books, 1955), pp. 103-14.

18. Some references on crop plants: André G. Haudricourt and Louis Hédin, *L'Homme et les plantes cultivées* (5ᵉ ed.; Paris: Gallimard, 1943); C. O. Sauer, *Agricultural Origins . . .* , ; R. Schnell, *Plantes alimentaires et vie agricole de l'Afrique Noire; essai de phytogéographie alimentaire* (Paris: Larose, 1957); C. O. Sauer, "Cultivated Plants . . ."; Jacques Barrau, *Polynesian and Micronesian Subsistence Agriculture* (Nouméa: South Pacific Commission, 1956); K. Heyne, *De nuttige planten van Indonesië* (3e druck. 2 vols.; 's-Gravenhage/Bandung, 1950); D. Bois, *Les plantes alimentaires chez tous les peuples à travers les ages* ("Encyclopédie biologique" [4 vols.; Paris: Lechevalier, 1927-37]); G. Watt, *A Dic-*

tionary of the Economic Products of India (6 vols.; Calcutta, India: 1889-1896); I. H. Burkill, *Dictionary of the Economic Products of the Malay Peninsula* (2 vols.; London: Oxford University Press, 1935); and J. C. Th. Uphof, *Dictionary of Economic Plants* (Weinheim, Germany: H. R. Engelmann [J. Cramer], 1959). A. de Candolle, *Origin of Cultivated Plants* (Reprinted from 2nd ed. of 1886; New York: Hafner Publishing Co., 1959), is a valuable source, though antiquated in many respects. Further references will be found in abundance in the works listed.

19. A good introduction to the study of agriculture can be found in E. Cecil Curwen and Gudmund Hatt, *Plow and Pasture; the Early History of Farming* (New York: Henry Schuman, Inc., 1956).

CHAPTER SEVEN

Artificial Environments

1. The Semang, like many of the more primitive groups, are in contact with outsiders (in this case, Malays, Sakai, Chinese, and occasionally Europeans), and some traits of the agricultural peoples have reached them. Some Semang groups, therefore, engage in cultivation. The same is true of such folk as the Philippine Negritos. See, for example, Paul Schebesta, *Bei den Urwaldzwergen von Malaya* (Leipzig, 1927), and Robert B. Fox, "The Pinatubo Negritos. Their Useful Plants and Material Culture," *Philippine Journal of Science,* LXXXI (1952), pp. 173-414.

The description of the life of peoples around the globe will, in accordance with ethnological practice, refer primarily to the "ethnographic present" rather than to strictly contemporary conditions. The baseline for such description varies from group to group, but corresponds approximately to the time of first massive European contact in most cases.

2. In biology, "synecology" is the study of relationships among living individuals in a community; "autecology" concerns the effects of environmental conditions, especially of climate and soil, upon individuals.

3. It appears that no one who has treated the subject of localization has employed the scheme that is used here. Amos O. Hawley, in *Human Ecology; a Theory of Community Structure* (New York: Ronald Press, 1950), makes occasional reference to locational factors, mainly in connection with commercial societies. A classic work by Charles H. Cooley, "The Theory of Transportation," *Publications of the American Economic Association,* IX (May 1894), pp. 1-148, has

strongly influenced the development of my concepts. Perhaps the most carefully reasoned nontechnical discussion of localization, again mainly applicable to commercial situations, is provided by Edgar M. Hoover, *The Location of Economic Activity* (New York: McGraw-Hill Book Co., 1948).

Since the purpose of the present chapter is primarily to put "common" knowledge into a particular order, few special sources may be invoked for the information used in building the ideas.

4. An interesting discussion of the concept of "resource" is found in Erich W. Zimmermann, *World Resources and Industries; a Functional Appraisal of the Availability of Agricultural and Industrial Materials* (Rev. ed.; New York: Harper & Bros., 1957). See also Alexander Spoehr, "Cultural differences in the interpretation of natural resources," in *Man's Role in Changing the Face of the Earth,* William L. Thomas, Jr., editor (Chicago: University of Chicago, 1956), pp. 93-102.

5. An excellent discussion is Chauncy D. Harris and Edward L. Ullmann, "The Nature of Cities," *Annals of the American Academy of Political and Social Science,* CCXLII (1945), pp. 7-17.

6. See Chauncy D. Harris, "A Functional Classification of Cities in the United States," *Geographical Review,* XXXIII (1943), pp. 86-99.

CHAPTER EIGHT

Ways of Livelihood

1. The ethnographic materials to which reference is made in this and the following chapter are from many scattered sources. The best single sources of information on all the groups considered and on others as well, are undoubtedly such great handbooks as R. Biasutti (ed.), *Le razze e i popoli della terra* (3d rev. ed., 4 vols.; Torino: Unione Tipografico-editrice Torinese, 1959). For certain restricted parts of the world other authoritative compilations are available, such as Julian H. Steward (ed.), *Handbook of South American Indians* (6 vols. Smithsonian Institution of Washington, Bureau of American Ethnology, Bulletin No. 143 [Washington: Smithsonian Institution, 1948]).

Except on doubtful points, the sources for particular statements will not be cited explicitly unless other than well-known standard sources have been consulted.

2. See especially Richard K. Beardsley *et al.,* "Functional and Evolutionary Implications of Community Patterning," *Memoirs of the*

Society for American Archaeology, No. 11 (1956), pp. 129-57 (Part 2 of *American Antiquity,* Vol. XXII, No. 2, 1956). Beardsley's types are: 1) Free wandering; 2) Restricted wandering; 3) Central based wandering; 4) Semi-permanent sedentary; 5) Simple nuclear centered; 6) Advanced nuclear centered; 7) Supra-nuclear integrated; 8) Incipient pastoral nomadic; 9) Equestrian hunting; and 10) Diversified pastoral nomadic. Of these, numbers 1 and 2 correspond to our "nomadic gathering" and "nomadic and semi-nomadic predation," respectively; number 3, to "semi-sedentary collecting"; numbers 4 and (in part) 5 to "shifting or sedentary subsistence cultivation"; number 5 (partly) to "sedentary peasant cultivation"; numbers 6 and 7 to "sedentary commerce" in several forms still to be discussed; numbers 8 and 10 to "nomadic pastoralism"; and number 9 to our "nomadic and semi-sedentary predation" as a special case, which Beardsley has introduced to account for the mounted Indians of Plains and Pampas.

Somewhat similar classifications are found in L. T. Hobhouse, G. C. Wheeler, and M. Ginsberg, *The Material Culture and Social Institutions of the Simpler Peoples* (London: Chapman and Hall, Ltd., 1930); C. Daryl Forde, *Habitat, Economy and Society: A Geographical Introduction to Ethnology* (London: Methuen & Co. Ltd., 1934); and Richard Thurnwald, *Economics in Primitive Communities* (London: Oxford University Press, 1932). George Peter Murdock's "World Ethnographic Sample," *American Anthropologist,* LIX (1957), pp. 664-87, lists traits for a large number of cultures, from which such classifications can readily be generated.

3. Apparently, no one has explicitly attempted to apply the notion of comparative advantage to the choices made by gathering peoples in the use of their territories. Perhaps this is because few people know much about these folk, and those who do are not the kind that wish to use economists' concepts and terminology. It would, nevertheless, be interesting to know how a group of, say, Semang, decide between harvesting fruit or chasing small game when both are available at the same time.

4. By far the best inventory of material artifacts of "primitive" peoples is found in André Leroi-Gourhan, *L'Homme et la matière* (Paris: Albin Michel, 1943) and *Milieu et techniques* (Paris: Albin Michel, 1945), where artifacts are treated comparatively, and their functions are analyzed.

5. There is some question as to whether the Tasmanians were able to kindle fire for themselves. Some writers have contended that the Andamanese were ignorant of fire-making. Both groups, at least, used "captured" fires of natural origin.

6. There is a very considerable literature on native contacts with outsiders, especially the whites. See William Christie McLeod, *The American Indian Frontier* (London: K. Paul, Trench, & Trubner;

New York: Alfred A. Knopf, Inc., 1928); Archibald Grenfell Price, *White Settlers and Native Peoples: An Historical Study of Racial Contacts between English-speaking Whites and Aboriginal Peoples in the United States, Canada, Australia, and New Zealand* (Melbourne: Georgian House, 1939); and Clive Turnbull, *Black War: The Extermination of the Tasmanian Aborigines* (London and Melbourne: F. W. Cheshire, 1948). The record for the English is more or less paralleled by those of the Spaniards, Portuguese, Russians, Dutch, and other peoples who have displaced tribal folk.

7. Sherburne F. Cook has made a remarkable reconstruction of the history of the decline of the California Indians during and since the Spanish period. Disease, enforced changes in diet, housing, sexual behavior, work, and other influences played their part. See Cook's "Population Trends among the California Mission Indians," *Ibero-Americana*, Vol. XVII (1940); "The Conflict between the California Indian and White Civilization: I. The Indian versus the Spanish Mission," *Ibero-Americana*, Vol. XXI (1943); ". . . II. The Physical and Demographic Reaction of the Non-Mission Indians in Colonial and Provincial California," *Ibero-Americana*, Vol. XXII (1943); and ". . . III. The American Invasion: 1848-1870," *Ibero-Americana*, Vol. XXIII (1943).

8. A. L. Kroeber, *Cultural and Natural Areas of Native North America* (Berkeley and Los Angeles: University of California Press, 1947), table 8, p. 142 and table 10, p. 144.

9. *Loc. cit.*

10. Cf. Omer N. Stewart, "Fire as the First Great Force Employed by Man," in William L. Thomas, Jr. (ed.), *Man's Role in Changing the Face of the Earth* (Chicago: University of Chicago Press, 1956), pp. 115-33.

11. On systems of cultivation, see especially E. Cecil Curwen and Gudmund Hatt, *Plow and Pasture; The Early History of Farming* (New York: Schuman, 1956), particularly Part II; Daniel Faucher, *Géographie agraire; types de cultures* (Paris: Médicis, 1949); and René Dumont, *Types of Rural Economy: Studies in World Agriculture* (London: Methuen & Co., Ltd., 1957).

12. Such ponded rice fields are inveterately referred to as "paddies," though that word actually applies only to the rice being grown in them, in its unhusked state. Perhaps a confusion with the word "paddock" is at the root of this widespread erroneous usage.

13. Harold C. Conklin, *Hanunoo Agriculture; A Report on an Integral System of Shifting Cultivation in the Philippines* (FAO Forestry Development Paper No. 12 [Rome: Food and Agricultural Organization, 1957]) proposes the name "swidden" for this kind of farming.

14. For an excellent study of shifting, or swidden, cultivation, cf. Conklin, *ibid.* See also Pierre de Schlippe, *Shifting Cultivation in*

Africa; The Zande System of Agriculture (London: Routledge & Kegan Paul Ltd., 1958).

15. Refer to Chapter 6, pp. 111-14, *supra*, for the distinctions between horticulture and agriculture.

16. For instance, refer to O. H. K. Spate, "Changing Native Agriculture in New Guinea," *Geographical Review*, XLIII (1953), pp. 151-72, and B. L. J. Bass, "Stone Age Agriculture in New Guinea," *Geographical Review*, XXXI (1941), pp. 555-69, for description of a horticultural system. Also see Jacques Barrau, *L'Agriculture vivrière autochtone de la Nouvelle Calédonie* (Nouméa: Commission du Pacifique Sud, 1956).

17. An impressive study of peasant farming in prewar Europe is Doreen Warriner, *Economics of Peasant Farming* (London: Oxford University Press, 1939), which includes much more on farming itself and on social conditions than the title indicates.

18. On commercial rotating agriculture, see for example Edward Higbee, *American Agriculture; Geography, Resources, Conservation* (New York: John Wiley & Sons; London: Chapman & Hall Ltd., 1958).

19. Cf. the acute observations of Homer Aschmann, "Hillside Farms, Valley Ranches, Land-clearing Costs and Settlement Patterns in South America," *Landscape*, V (Winter, 1955-1956), pp. 17-24.

20. Robert Redfield, like many of his predecessors among the students of peasant life, insists upon the co-existence of urban and rural, or folk, sections as a necessary condition of peasant societies. See his *The Primitive World and Its Transformations* (Ithaca, N. Y.: Cornell University Press, 1953) and *Peasant Society and Culture; An Anthropological Approach to Civilization* (Chicago: University of Chicago Press, 1956). It is well known, however, that among such peoples as the North African Berbers, the marketing and service functions that are complementary with rural peasant activities are carried on in periodic markets held at uninhabited meeting places, often at shrines or in neutral territory. See Francisco Benet, "Explosive Markets: The Berber Highlands" in Karl Polanyi, Conrad M. Arensberg, and Harry W. Pearson (eds.), *Trade and Market in the Early Empires: Economies in History and Theory* (Glencoe, Ill.: The Free Press and Falcon's Wing Press, 1957), pp. 188-217; and Marvin W. Mikesell, "The Role of Tribal Markets in Morocco: Examples from the Northern Zone," *Geographical Review*, XLVIII (1959), pp. 454-511.

21. For densities in Sumatra, cf. Pierre Gourou, *Les pays tropicaux; principes d'une géographie humaine et économique* (Paris: Presses Universitaires de France, 1948), p. 43.

22. For Zande densities, cf. DeSchlippe, *op. cit.*

23. Examples of the variety of plant products used by cultivators are given in Conklin, *op. cit.* and Philip L. Wagner, *Nicoya: A Cul-*

tural Geography (University of California Publications in Geography, XII, pp. 195-250 [Berkeley and Los Angeles: University of California Press, 1958]).

24. See for instance Lawrence L. Krader, "Principles and Structures in the Organization of the Asiatic Steppe-pastoralists," *Southwestern Journal of Anthropology*, XI (Summer, 1955), pp. 67-92; and "Ecology of Central Asian Pastoralism," *Southwestern Journal of Anthropology*, XI (Winter, 1955), pp. 301-26.

CHAPTER NINE

The Commercial Environment

1. Max Weber, *General Economic History*, trans. Frank H. Knight (Glencoe, Ill.: The Free Press, 1950). On techniques under this system, see Charles Singer, E. J. Holmyard, A. R. Hall and Trevor I. Williams (eds.), *A History of Technology*, Vols. II, III (London: Oxford University Press, 1951).

2. The organizing principles of modern industrial production are the subject of an extensive literature in the fields of industrial management, production engineering, industrial architecture, and production economics. For an interesting overview of the historical development of this kind of production, see Siegfried Giedion, *Mechanization Takes Command; A Contribution to Anonymous History* (New York: Oxford University Press, 1948) and Singer *et al.* (eds.), *op. cit.*, Vols. IV and V in particular. The engineer's viewpoint is nicely presented in Frank G. Woolard, *Principles of Mass and Flow Production* (London: Iliffe & Sons Ltd., 1954).

3. The technical literature of manufacturing is readily available; I shall give no references here.

4. "Rationalization" in this sense should not be confused with the portioning out of different specialties to different geographic areas, for which the term is also sometimes used.

5. The whole operation is performed automatically in this case of so-called "transfer machines."

6. Among other things, the variety of choices of routes and combinations of routes that are possible is so large that in the United States there must be an astronomical number of different books of freight rates to cover all classes of shipments over all possible routes.

7. This idea has been worked out in great detail for the Chicago area by Allen K. Philbrick in "Principles of Areal Functional Organization in Regional Human Geography," *Economic Geography*, XXXIII (1957), pp. 299-336. See also John E. Brush, "The Hierarchy of

Places in Southwestern Wisconsin," *Geographical Review,* XLIII (1953), pp. 380-402; and John E. Brush and Howard E. Bracey, "Rural Centers in Southwestern Wisconsin and Southern England," *Geographical Review,* LXV (1955), pp. 559-69.

8. Many of the more significant topics with which the ensuing sections of this chapter deal are of especial appeal to American geographers, and the literature of the field abounds with studies on them. Preston E. James and Clarence F. Jones (eds.), *American Geography: Inventory and Prospect* (Syracuse: Syracuse University Press, 1954) provides an introduction to the topics of my discussion in the following chapters: "Settlement Geography" and "Urban Geography" on settlements; "The Geography of Resources"; "Agricultural Geography"; "The Geography of Manufacturing"; and "Transportation Geography." As will be seen from these summaries, almost all of the American work on these topics has dealt with situations in the industrial-commercial countries. For the most recent publications, the reader may consult current and late issues of such journals as *Economic Geography, Geographical Review, Journal of Geography, Landscape,* and the *Annals of the Association of American Geographers.* Similar journals are published in several other countries besides the United States.

9. The diversity of California agriculture is displayed in a most fascinating pamphlet, L. A. Crawford and Edgar B. Hurd, "Types of Farming in California, Analyzed by Enterprises" (University of California Agricultural Experiment Station Bulletin 654 [September 1941]).

10. Andrew Gunder Frank, "General Productivity in Soviet Agriculture and Industry: The Ukraine, 1928-55," *Journal of Political Economy,* LXVI (December, 1958), pp. 498-515.

CHAPTER TEN

A Geographic Outlook

1. A little reflection on the matter is enough to make clear the cumulative nature of these features. We know that cultivators are still in part also hunters and gatherers, and that the more successfully a man fills his role as a commercial producer in our own society (or the more he is paid for it), the greater is the tendency for him to hunt in distant forests, fish in distant waters, or cultivate large gardens. Perhaps if this cumulative quality of livelihood forms had been given due attention, the old idea of "stages of evolution" of livelihood

would have been expressed rather as "additions to existing livelihood mechanisms." The tendency here, as in many alleged "evolutions," is toward diversification, rather than toward successive displacements.

2. *Schinus Molle,* Vol. L.

3. The problem of environmental limitation is much discussed among anthropologists today. Cf. Betty Jane Meggers, "Environmental Limitations on the Development of Culture," *American Anthropologist,* LVI (October, 1954), pp. 801-24, and the reaction to this article in Edwin J. Ferdon, Jr., "Agricultural Potential and the Development of Cultures," *Southwestern Journal of Anthropology,* XV (Spring, 1959), pp. 1-19; and Milton Altschuler, "On the Environmental Limitations of Mayan Cultural Development," *Southwestern Journal of Anthropology,* XIV (Summer, 1958), pp. 189-98. Among other anthropological writings on this subject see the papers of Julian H. Steward collected in his *Theory of Culture Change: The Methodology of Multilinear Evolution* (Urbana: University of Illinois Press, 1955); Joseph B. Birdsell, "Some Environmental and Cultural Factors Influencing the Structuring of Australian Aboriginal Populations," *American Naturalist,* LXXXVII, 1953, pp. 171-207; and A. L. Kroeber, *Cultural and Natural Areas of Native North America* (Berkeley and Los Angeles: University of California Press, 1947).

INDEX